GAYME...
COUNTY
GUIDES

East Sussex

First published by
Gaymer's Guides Limited,
24 Notting Hill Gate, London W11 3BR
Tel: 071-229 9944 Fax: 071-727 5442

Copyright © Gaymer's Guides Ltd. 1990
Gaymer's County Guides to East Sussex
ISBN 1-872173-01-2

British Library Cataloguing in Publication Data
Gaymer, Stephen Benjamin 1952-
East Sussex.
1. East Sussex - Visitors' guides
I. Title
914.22504858
ISBN 1-872173-01-2

Editor: Stephen Gaymer
Text: Rob Raeburn
Assistant Editor: Alison Ritchie
Original Design: Angel Bacon

Cover photograph
The Seven Sisters

Printed by Whitstable Litho Printers Ltd., Whitstable, Kent.
Typeset in Palatino by Area Graphics, Letchworth.

The publishers would like to thank the
following for their assistance in the compilation of this guide:
Edward Crawshaw, Sebastian Grimes, English Heritage,
Andrew Lucas, John Stimpson,The National Trust.
Gaymer's Girls: Rose Bellingham, Sue Bushnell,
Sarah Chamberlain, Cythare Cooper,
Vicki-Jane Fuller, Lucy Gaymer.

CONTENTS

KEY TO ABBREVIATIONS

AA.	AUTOMOBILE ASSOCIATION	DOGS.	DOGS ALLOWED	RAC.	ROYAL AUTOMOBILE CLUB
AC.	ACCESS	ER.	EGON RONAY	V.	VISA
AM.	AMERICAN EXPRESS	F.	FUNCTIONS	VEG.	VEGETARIAN FOOD
B.	BANQUETS	M.	MICHELIN GUIDE		AVAILABLE
CF.	CONFERENCE FACILITIES	N/S.	NO SMOKING AREAS	W.	WEDDINGS
D.	DINERS CLUB	P.	PARTIES	W/CHAIR.	WHEELCHAIR ACCESS

THE ROYAL PAVILION, BRIGHTON (PAGE 18)

GAYMER'S COUNTY GUIDES are the first fully-illustrated comprehensive guide books that contain a gazetteer of every town, village and hamlet within a given area; they also list every hotel, guest house, restaurant and pub within that area, plus places of interest and churches. Other amenities are also included, such as art galleries, leisure and garden centres, cinemas and theatres, and so on. In short, Gaymer's County Guides list everything that may be of interest to visitors.

There are many publications which list some of these facilities, but none that list them all; they also tend to be selective. Gaymer's County Guides list everything, without qualification. However, by giving more details of certain establishments, it is left to the readers' discretion to decide whether a particular place suits their requirements.

At the back of the book are detailed indexes; the towns, the places of interest and illustrations are indexed alphabetically. Other amenities are cross-referenced, so that should a specific amenity be sought, for example a swimming-pool, it can be located.

The majority of establishments whose full details appear have paid a fee, and will have copies of this guide for sale. Although every effort has been made to include every establishment, there will inevitably be places that have been overlooked. We invite readers to send in details of omissions or inaccuracies. (See form page 125)

Our aim is to produce a fully comprehensive and accurate representation of every relevant amenity in the county, that will serve as an invaluable aid to tourists and inhabitants alike.

MAN HAS INHABITED the south-east of England since Neolithic times, arriving by sea from France and the continent, and introducing skills and customs into the local culture. He has built camps, castles, villas, places of worship and palaces, some of which remain today. The Neolithic causewayed camps at **Jevington** and **Selmeston**, the Norman castles of **Lewes, Hastings**, and **Pevensey**, and the spectacular medieval castles of **Bodiam** and **Herstmonceux**, the magnificent **Battle Abbey** and the eccentric **Brighton Pavilion**.

The word Sussex is derived from 'South Saxons', and was an entity before the Doomsday Book in 1086 documented the Kingdom, and it wasn't until 1889 that the large county of Sussex, with its 70 miles of coastline, was divided up into East and West by Royal Charter. In 1974 the boundaries were changed again by the Government, to even-out the voting areas.

Sussex can be divided neatly into three distinct sections; to the north, running east to west, the **Weald**; to the south the **broad coastal plain**, running parallel to the **English Channel**, and sandwiched between them, and finally running out into the sea at Eastbourne, the famous **South Downs**.

It is impossible to write about East Sussex without reference to its coastal position in the south-east of England, and its close proximity to France and the continent. For it is its defences that will be tested first by any would-be invader, and indeed **William the Conqueror**, landed near **Pevensey**, and fought and defeated King Harold at that most decisive **Battle of Hastings**, in, as every schoolboy knows, 1066. The course of English history was inexorably changed by that invasion, but William was the last of a long line of invaders going back into prehistory, and including the most successful of all, the Romans, who also landed near **Pevensey**; **Julius Caesar** was reputed to have stayed at **Pevensey Castle**. In order to quell the ambitions of further invaders, the **Cinque Ports** were fortified in the Middle Ages, of which **Hastings** became the premier port, and both **Winchelsea** and **Rye** were later members, and **Seaford** and **Pevensey** became non-corporate members.

Whereas much of the coast of **West Sussex** has been eroded, in **East Sussex** the reverse is true. Those important ports of yesteryear, **Hastings, Rye** and **Winchelsea** are now some distance inland from their original sites, and their harbours are silted up. The threat of invasion has persisted right up to modern times, and it is now known that the spearhead of Hitler's planned invasion was near **Rye**.

Many modern Sussex inhabitants commute every day into London. This has bestowed on Sussex an opulence that it would find difficult to support alone, and many of the carefully preserved farmhouses and cottages owe their continuing prosperity to salaries earned outside the county.

The **Weald**, in particular, reflects this phenomena. The word weald comes from the Anglo Saxon meaning 'wood', as all this part of the country was once one vast forest until it was cleared for agricultural purposes, and to fuel the iron workers' furnaces. To the north of the county is **Ashdown Forest**, very much larger than now, and many of its trees too were felled to fuel the ironworkers fires, from Roman times until the 18th century.

Once a major thoroughfare for prehistoric man, the **South Downs Way** follows the line of the hills from Hampshire all the way to **Eastbourne**, and the path is still well-trodden by modern day walkers. Never more than a couple of miles wide, the downs have for centuries played an important part in the region's history. There are views all around from the top of the downs, and Neolithic man built hill forts there.

Nearly every coastal village has connections, real or perceived, with smuggling, and it is obvious that much of it went on. From **Fishbourne** to **Rye**, many an illicit substance has been secretly rowed ashore to hidden coves at night.

Sussex-by-the-Sea has long invoked visions of holidays, and the coast is now almost completely devoted to the pursuit of leisure and retirement. There are the well-known holiday resorts of **Brighton, Eastbourne, Bexhill** and **St. Leonards** that offer all the traditional sea-side activities of sailing, swimming and fishing. East Sussex also has some of the most striking chalk cliffs where the south Downs give way to the sea, and sights of **Beachy Head** and the **Seven Sisters** are truly enduring.

BEACHY HEAD

THE CLERGY HOUSE, THE FIRST BUILDING ACQUIRED BY THE NATIONAL TRUST

ALFRISTON

Three miles from the sea, Alfriston, lying between the downs and the Cuckmere river, is suffused with tales of smugglers. In the early 19th century the tough Alfriston Gang, led by one Stanton Collins, used Cuckmere Cove for their illegal operations, and dealt ruthlessly with anyone trying to stop them. In modern times, this charming village is full of souvenirs and relics, antique shops and tea-rooms. On the main street there are some fine timbered buildings, particularly the old inns, the George and the Ship. The Star Inn is one of the oldest in England and was founded as a hostel for mendicant friars; the rectory, Clergy House, a wattle-and-daub building, dating from the 14th century, was the first building to be acquired by the National Trust in 1896, for £10. Behind the main street the great green runs up to the majestic 14th century parish church, St Andrew, which stands on a Saxon barrow. The market cross, one of only two in Sussex (the other is at Chichester) has been buffeted by time and traffic, and had to be rebuilt after being demolished by a lorry.

Population: 811.

PLACES OF INTEREST

Clergy House

Tel: (0323) 870001

The first building acquired by the National Trust in 1896, for £10. Possibly a parish priest's house, c. 1350.

Months Open: April - October. Days Open: Every day. Hours Open: 11am - 6pm (sunset if earlier). Admission: £1. Children half price. Unsuitable for wheelchairs. No dogs.

Saxon Cemetery

On top of a hill to the north-west of the village is a pagan Saxon cemetery which has yielded many fine artefacts mainly from the fifth century, but some from the Roman era. There is also a very fine long barrow about a mile to the west and a round barrow two miles west of the church.

HOTELS

Deans Place Hotel

BN26 5TW. Tel: (0323) 870248

The George Inn

High Street. Tel: (0323) 870319

Riverdale Private Hotel

Seaford Road. Tel: (0323) 870397

Rose Cottage Inn

Tel: (0323) 870377

THE GEORGE INN, ALFRISTON

Star Inn
High Street. Tel: (0323) 870495
Wingrove Tavern and Restaurant
High Street. Tel: (0323) 870276

RESTAURANTS
Moonrakers Restaurant
High Street. BN26 5TD Tel: (0323) 870472
The Tudor House Restaurant
The Tudor House. Tel: (0323) 870891
The White Lodge Country House Hotel
Sloe Lane. Tel: (0323) 870265/870284

PUBLIC HOUSES
The Golden Galleon
Exceat Bridge , Exceat. Tel: (0323) 892247
The Smugglers Inn
Market Cross. Tel: (0323) 870241

CAFÉS & TEA ROOMS
Chestnut Tea Rooms
8 High Street. Tel: (0323) 870298
Old Saddlers Tea Shop
Saddlers House , High Street. Tel: (0323) 870434

OTHER AMENITIES
ART GALLERY
Alfriston Gallery
Alfriston House, High Street. Tel: (0323) 870631

HOSTEL
Youth Hostels Association
Frog Firle. Tel: (0323) 870423

ZOOS
Drusillas Tel: (0323) 870234
The Living World
Exceat Barn , Exceat. Tel: (0323) 870100

AMBERSTONE

CAFÉ/TEA ROOMS
Rosemary Orchard Cafe
Tel: (0323) 843284

OTHER AMENITY
HOSPITAL
Amberstone Hospital
Carters Corner. Tel: (0323) 841593

≈ ≈ ≈ ≈ ≈ ≈ ≈

ARLINGTON
A quaint and tiny hamlet, worth a visit as much for the winding lanes you follow to reach it, as for the village itself. The remarkable church, however, is a bonus for any traveller who makes the detour.
Population: 682 .

PUBLIC HOUSES
The Old Oak Inn
Cane Heath . Tel: (032 12) 2072
The Yew Tree Inn
Tel: (0323) 870590

≈ ≈ ≈ ≈ ≈ ≈ ≈

ASHURST WOOD
South-east of East Grinstead, the village lies on the county border between East and West Sussex. There are some grand houses in the area, including one, Barton St Mary, by Lutyens.

PUBLIC HOUSES
The Maypole Inn
76 Maypole Road. Tel: (034 282) 4108
The Three Crowns
10 Hammerwood Road. Tel: (0342) 321597

OTHER AMENITIES
HEALTH CLUB
Natural Health Clinic
Hammerwood Road. Tel: (034 282) 4705

RIDING SCHOOL
Shovelstrode Riding School
Homestall Road. Tel: (0342) 323153

TAXI
Dial-A-Car
111 Hammerwood Road. Tel: (034 282) 3265

≈ ≈ ≈ ≈ ≈ ≈ ≈

THE DOWNS LOOKING TOWARDS ALFRISTON, WITH FIRLE BEACON IN THE BACKGROUND

BARCOMBE

Most visitors come for the swimming and boating on the Ouse at Barcombe Mills, but the churchyard is worth a visit for the magnificent view of the downs. This part of the Ouse was known as the Iron River, because of the number of forges and furnaces which were here as late as the 17th century, as part of Sussex's important iron industry.

Population: 1,420.

PLACES OF INTEREST

Shelley's Folly

17th century brick house with fine cartouche of the Shelley arms, situated a mile and a quarter to the north-west of the village.

HOTEL

The Anchor Inn (right)

Anchor Lane. Tel: (0273) 400414

The Anchor Inn is situated beside the River Ouse in lovely unspoiled rural Sussex and boats are available for hire.

BEDROOMS: 1 Single, (1 TV, 1 tea/coffee) B&B £ 25.00. 4 Double, (1 en suite, 3 TV,) B&B £ 40.00 - £ 48.00. 1 Twin. RESTAURANT: Tea: £ 2.50. Dinner: £ 15.00.

PUBLIC HOUSES

The Anglers Rest

Barcombe Mills. Tel: (0273) 400270

The Royal Oak

Barcombe Cross. Tel: (0273) 400418

CAFÉ/TEA ROOMS

The Old Mill

Barcombe Mills. Tel: (0273) 400442

BATTLE ABBEY, BUILT BY WILLIAM THE CONQUEROR AS A THANKSGIVING FOR HIS VICTORY

BATTLE

About five and a half miles north-west of Hastings, this is the site of the beginning of the last successful invasion of Britain. The battle commemorated is of course the Battle of Hastings (or more appropriately, the Battle of Battle), perhaps the most significant ever fought on British soil, and the date, 1066, is one etched into every schoolchild's memory.

The town itself has a pleasant Georgian High Street, and there is a windmill on the summit of Mount Street, the old London road. The great gatehouse of the abbey, built by William in thanks for his victory, looms over the market square. There is a museum in the town housing a diorama illustrating the battle.

Population: 5,049.

PLACES OF INTEREST

Battle Abbey
Tel: (04246) 3792

The best known date in English history - 1066 and the Battle of Hastings. Built by William the Conqueror as a thanksgiving for his victory. The church has yet to be fully excavated but visitors may walk over the battlefield, and see the remains of many of the domestic buildings of the monastery and watch a film on the battle.

Months Open: All year. Days Open: Every day. Hours Open: 10am - 6pm. Bank Holidays: Closed Xmas. Admission: £1.60. Children half price.

Battle Museum
Facing the Abbey Gateway. Battle of Hastings Diorama and reproduction of the Bayeux Tapestry. Roman-British remains from local sites.

Months Open: Easter - September. Days Open: Every day. Hours Open: 10am - 1pm, 2 - 5pm. Sundays 2.30 - 5.30pm. Admission: 30p. Children 10p.

Museum of Shops and Social History
Tel: (042 46) 4269

A collection of packaging and social history items, displayed authentically in Victorian Streets.

Months Open: All year. Days Open: Everyday (except between January -March). Hours Open: 10am- 5.30pm (except November -December 10.30am - 4.30pm) .

HOTELS

The Chequers
Lower Lake. Tel: (042 46) 2088

George & Dragon Inn
School Hill. Tel: (042 46) 4466

La Vieille Auberge
27 High Street. Tel: (042 46) 2255

Netherfield Place
Netherfield Place. TN33 9PP. Tel: (042 46) 4455

Powder Mills
Powder Mill Lane. TN33 0SP. Tel: (042 46) 2035/4540

Imposing Georgian country house hotel in 150 acres on site of 1066 Battle. Beautiful walks and fishing lakes. All rooms en suite.

BEDROOMS: 2 Single, (2 en suite, 2 TV, 2 phone, 2 tea/coffee) B&B £ 30.00. 4 Double, (4 en suite, 4 TV, 4 phone, 4 tea/coffee) B&B £ 50.00 - £ 65.00. 6 Twin, (6 en suite, 6 TV, 6 phone, 6 tea/ coffee) B&B £ 50.00 - £ 55.00. 1 Family, (1 en suite, 1 TV, 1 phone, 1 tea/coffee) £ 70.00. 1 Four Poster. RESTAURANT: English Cuisine. HOTEL INFORMATION: CF. W.

RESTAURANTS

Battle Fryers
67 High Street. Tel: (042 46) 4751

The Bayeux Restaurant
31 Mount Street. Tel: (042 46) 2132

Original & adventurous Cuisine. Specialities: McCabe's Lament, One in the Eye, Smoked Salmon Bayeux Style,Chicken Malahide. Hours Open: Lunch: 12pm-2pm. Dinner: 7pm-10pm. Closed Dec 25th-Dec27th. Lunch: £ 12.50. Dinner: £ 12.50. House Wine: £ 7.25. Credit Cards: Ac. Am. D. V. Seating Capacity: 40. Veg. W/chair acc. B. P. W.

The Blacksmiths Restaurant
43 High Street. Tel: (042 46) 3200

Bonani Tandoori Restaurant & Takeaway
42b High Street. Tel: (042 46) 2677

China Garden
44 High Street. Tel: (042 46) 2046

Pilgrims Rest
High Street. Tel: (042 46) 2314

Priory House
17 High Street. Tel: (042 46) 3366

Senlac Hotel
Lower Lake. Tel: (042 46) 2034

PUBLIC HOUSES

The 1066
High Street. Tel: (042 46) 3224

Abbey Hotel
High Street. Tel: (042 46) 2755

Ye Olde Kings Head
Mount Street. Tel: (042 46) 2317

The Netherfield Arms
Tel: (042 482) 282

The Red Lion
Denbigh Road, Hooe. Tel: (0424) 892371

The Squirrel Inn
North Trade Road. Tel: (042 46) 2717

CAFÉ/TEA ROOMS

Bayeux Cottage Tea Rooms
11 Mount Street. Tel: (042 46) 2593

OTHER AMENITIES

ART GALLERY
Alex Gerrard Fine Art Ltd.
2 Abbey Green. Tel: (042 46) 4204

CAR HIRE/SELF DRIVE
Battle Hill Service Station
Battle Hill. Tel: (042 46) 4416

Vicarys of Battle Ltd.
32 High Street. Tel: (042 46) 2425

CARAVAN PARKS
Caravan Club Ltd.
Normanhurst Court, Stevens Crouch. Tel: (042 46) 3808

Crowhurst Park Caravans
Crowhurst Park. Tel: (042 46) 3344/5

GARDEN CENTRE
Sunny Rise Nurseries
North Trade Road. Tel: (042 46) 2685

HOSPITAL
Battle Hospital
North Trade Road. Tel: (042 46) 2030

LEISURE CENTRE
Battle Area Sports Centre
Claverham Community College, North Trade Road.
TN33 0HT Tel: (042 46) 4772

TAXIS
Battle Car Hire
107 Coronation Gardens. Tel: (042 46) 3485
Battle Station Taxis
Battle Station, Station Road. Tel: (042 46) 2222
M. Coles
Alfric, Lewins Croft, Mount Street. Tel: (042 46) 2082
E. Harris
Oaktree Cottage, Marley Lane. Tel: (042 46) 2620

TOURIST OFFICE
Battle Tourist Information Centre
88 High Street. Tel: (042 46) 3721

🐾 🐾 🐾 🐾 🐾 🐾 🐾

BECKLEY
The town was bequeathed to a kinsman by King Alfred. It is said to be haunted by the clatter of the galloping hooves of the horse of Sir Reginald Fitzurse, one of the murderers of Thomas à Becket, who tried to claim sanctuary in the church. At one time the town boasted a thriving glass furnace, which had previously produced cannons.
Population: 920.

HOTEL
Royal Oak
Tel: (079 726) 312

PUBLIC HOUSE
The Rose & Crown
Northiam Road. Tel: (079 74) 2161

OTHER AMENITY
WILDLIFE PARK
The Childrens Farm
Great Knelle Farm. Tel: (079 726) 321/347

🐾 🐾 🐾 🐾 🐾 🐾 🐾

BERWICK
Pronounced 'Ber-wick' and situated on a dead end, it is worth a visit for the modern paintings in the church.
Population: 224.

PUBLIC HOUSE
The Berwick Inn
Tel: (0323) 870002

OTHER AMENITIES
GARDEN CENTRE
Allseason Landscapes
3 Princes Field. Tel: (0323) 870875

RAILWAY STATION
Berwick Station
Tel: (0323) 870355

🐾 🐾 🐾 🐾 🐾 🐾 🐾

BEXHILL-ON-SEA
Like much of the Sussex coast, the old village stands on a hill behind the new town, and this is where the parish church of St. Peter is to be found. Bexhill was late in becoming a resort, not really starting till about 1880. It has no pier, but the De La Warr Pavilion is one of the earliest examples of a multi-purpose fun palace in Britain.
Population: 34,772.

PLACES OF INTEREST
Bexhill Museum
Tel: (0424) 211769
Housed in an Edwardian shelter hall with views over Egerton Park and lake. Displays include the local archaeology, geology and marine biology.
Months Open: All year. Days Open: Tuesdays - Sundays. Hours Open: Tues - Fri, 10am - 5pm; Sat - Sun 2 - 5pm. Admission: 40p. Children half price. Easy roadside parking. Suitable for the disabled, wheelchairs unavailable.
Bexhill Museum of Costume & Social History
Manor House Gardens, Old Town.
Tel: (0424) 215361/211711
A museum showing the costume and couture through the ages.
Months Open: Easter - September. Days Open: Tuesday - Sunday. Hours Open: 10.30am - 1pm, 2 -5.30pm; Sat- Sun 2.30 -5.30pm. Admission: 60p. Children half Price. Prices are subject to revision.

HOTELS
Beaulieu Hotel
36 Eversley Road. Tel: (0424) 215253

Bedford Lodge Hotel
3 Bedford Avenue. TN40 1ND. Tel: (0424) 730097

Bell Hotel
Church Street, Old Town. TN40 2HE. Tel: (0424) 219654

Castle Hotel
Town Hall Square. Tel: (0424) 211730

Dunselma Hotel
25 Marina. Tel: (0424) 212988

Hotel Saint Norberts
97 De La Warr Road. Tel: (0424) 219115

Leahyrst Hotel
9 Bedford Avenue. Tel: (0424) 219906

Lilburn Residential Hotel
7 Albany Road. Tel: (0424) 215100

Mount Hotel
1a Cantelupe Road. Tel: (0424) 221650

Nether Laggan Residential Hotel
31/39 Eversley Road. Tel: (0424) 212979

Northern Hotel
76 Sea Road. Tel: (0424) 212836

Park Lodge Hotel
16 Egerton Road. TN39 3HH. Tel: (0424) 216547

Radclive Private Hotel
36 Woodville Road. Tel: (0424) 212007

The Rangers Hotel
4 Brassey Road. Tel: (0424) 212705

Victoria Hotel (Bexhill)
1 Middlesex Road. Tel: (0424) 210382

GUEST HOUSES

The Arosa Guest House
6 Albert Road. Tel: (0424) 212574

Avalon Guest House
1 Rotherfield Avenue. Tel: (0424) 216441

Buenos Aires
24 Albany Road. Tel: (0424) 212269

Linden Guest House
9 Woodville Road. Tel: (0424) 224621

Nelson Guest House
6 Station Road. Tel: (0424) 214063
Happy, homely and spotless.
Months Open: 12. Number of Bedrooms: 8. B&B per person:
£11. TV. Pets welcome. 10 space car park. Garden. Proprietor:
Mrs PJ Russell.

Sea Breeze Guest House
65 Egerton Road. Tel: (0424) 225952

RESTAURANTS

Alex's Spaghetteria
55 Marina. Tel: (0424) 730751

Box Tree
11/13 Wickham Avenue. Tel: (0424) 210435

Continental Restaurant
43 Marina. TW40 1BQ Tel: (0424) 210145

The Copper Kettle
30 Station Road. Tel: (0424) 210926

Corianders Health Food Restaurant
66 Devonshire Road. Tel: (0424) 220329

Criterion Restaurant
12 Western Road. Tel: (0424) 211009

Fortes Ice Cream Parlour
47 Marina. Tel: (0424) 212141

Friar Tuck
70 London Road. Tel: (0424) 211357

Garcia's Pizza
18 Station Road. Tel: (0424) 220728

The Golden Fish Bar
7 Sea Road. Tel: (0424) 210685

The Lantern Restaurant
57 Sackville Road. Tel: (0424) 220325

Little Marabou
58 Devonshire Road. Tel: (0424) 215052

Louis Fish Bar (Take Away)
36 Sea Road. Tel: (0424) 223060

Lychgates Restaurant
5a Church Street. Tel: (0424) 212193

The Marabou Restaurant
60 Devonshire Road. Tel: (0424) 212189

Merry Muncher Restaurant
43 Western Road. Tel: (0424) 211401

Ming Hwa Restaurant
26 Sackville Road. Tel: (0424) 215509

Miramar Tea Rooms
De La Warr Parade. Tel: (0424) 220360

Nell Gwynne Restaurant
11 Marina Arcade. Tel: (0424) 219981

Nicks Restaurant Francais
5 Brassey Road. Tel: (0424) 212705

Oven Door
2 Buckhurst Place. Tel: (0424) 222935

Paramount Kitchen Chinese Takeaway
103 London Road. Tel: (0424) 211636

The Pumpkin
26 Devonshire Road. Tel: (0424) 211188

Rose of Bengal
66 London Road. Tel: (0424) 224225/225066

Seven Seas Fish & Chips
52 Ninfield Road. Tel: (0424) 215043

Shiplu Tandoori Restaurant
109 London Road. Tel: (0424) 219159/219677

The Square Fish Bar
21 London Road. Tel: (0424) 214822

Sun Wah Chinese Take Away
44 Ninfield Road. Tel: (0424) 210149

Tastyway Takeaway
15 Station Road. Tel: (0424) 223736

Trawlers
60 Sackville Road. Tel: (0424) 210227

Viking Fish Bar
127 London Road. Tel: (0424) 216771

PUBLIC HOUSES

Becketts Bar
35 Devonshire Road. Tel: (0424) 223950
The Devonshire Public House
Devonshire Square. Tel: (0424) 219413
Royal Sovereign
15 Sea Road. Tel: (0424) 213427
Shunters
Terminus Road. Tel: (0424) 217647
The Sportsman Public House
15 Sackville Road. Tel: (0424) 214214
Traffers Bar
Egerton Road. Tel: (0424) 210240
The Turkey
Turkey Road. Tel: (0424) 214625
Wilton Court Lounge Bar
Wilton Road. Tel: (0424) 210208/216364
The York
London Road. Tel: (0424) 224275

CAFÉS & TEA ROOMS

The Coffee Pot
5 Endwell Road. Tel: (0424) 730078
Cookies Cafe
1A Buxton Drive. Tel: (0424) 218292
Cosy Cafe
123 London Road. Tel: (0424) 222137
Di Paolo Cafe
5 Marina. Tel: (0424) 210337
Seashells Tearooms
54 Western Road. Tel: (0424) 730019
Sovereign Light Cafe
West Parade. Tel: (0424) 222136
The Cafe
114 Ninfield Road. Tel: (0424) 219603

OTHER AMENITIES

ART GALLERY
Stewart Gallery
48 Devonshire Road. Tel: (0424) 223410

BUS & COACH SERVICES
Bexhill Community Bus
38 Sackville Road. Tel: (0424) 222820
Hastings & District Transport Ltd.
43 Western Road. Tel: (0424) 217121

CAR HIRE/SELF DRIVE
Bexhill Self Drive
Wellington Place, Terminus Road. Tel: (0424) 217715
Honda Car Centre

Honda House, 5-7 Beeching Road. Tel: (0424) 221330
Phillimore Hire Drive
1a Beeching Road. Tel: (0424) 217584
Skinners (Bexhill) Ltd.
57-69 London Road. Tel: (0424) 212001/212000
Wallace & Co.
Terminus Road. Tel: (0424) 217715

CINEMA
The Curzon Leisure Centre
Western Road. Tel: (0424) 210078

GARDEN CENTRE
E. Warburton & Sons
41-43 Station Road. TN40 1RG Tel: (0424) 211560

HEALTH CLUB
Physiques
21a Wilton Road. Tel: (0424) 211760

HOSPITAL
Bexhill Hospital
Holliers Hill. Tel: (0424) 730077

SNOOKER CENTRES
Bexhill Snooker Centre
96 London Road. Tel: (0424) 220564
Clarkson Leisure
12 Wickham Avenue. Tel: (0424) 222586

STORES
Woolworths plc
44 Devonshire Road. Tel: (0424) 219409

TAXIS
Advance Taxis
59 Ninfield Road. Tel: (0424) 224999
D.E. Armstrong
3/17 Dorset Road South. Tel: (0424) 219077
Atlas Car Hire
14 Leasingham Gardens. Tel: (0424) 211392
Bexhill Taxicare
38 Salisbury Road. Tel: (0424) 224746
Bexhill Taxis
55 Ridgewood Gardens. Tel: (0424) 218805
Bobs Cabs
8 Christine Close. Tel: (0424) 223018
Brians Private Hire
30 Barrack Road. Tel: (0424) 221733
Cabbex Private Hire
8 Terminus Road. Tel: (0424) 222737
Central Taxis
Murco Filling Station, Buchurst Road. Tel: (0424) 22067
Devonshire Square Taxis

BODIAM CASTLE WAS BUILT TO GUARD AN IMPORTANT CROSSING OF THE RIVER ROTHER

Devonshire Square. Tel: (0424) 223225
G & R Eldred
87 Reginald Road. Tel: (0424) 217282
Executive Cars
70 Collington Lane East. Tel: (0424) 217240
Grey Cars
29 Collington Lane East. Tel: (0424) 730933
Johns Taxis
51 Edmonton Road. Tel: (0424) 217271
Sidley Cabs
1 Sidley Street. Tel: (0424) 223000
Taxi-Travel
4 Windsor Road. Tel: (0424) 214991

THEATRE
De La Warr Pavilion
Marina. Tel: (0424) 212023/212022/219678

🐌 🐌 🐌 🐌 🐌 🐌 🐌

BLACKBOYS

Between Uckfield to the west and Heathfield. There is a youth hostel north of the village.

PUBLIC HOUSES
Blackboys Inn

Lewes Road. Tel: (082 582) 283
The Crown Inn
High Street. Tel: (082 582) 273

🐌 🐌 🐌 🐌 🐌 🐌 🐌

BODIAM

Pronounced locally as 'Bodgem', it sits on the Kent border, between the River Rother and the Kent Ditch. In the Middle Ages the castle was built to guard an important crossing of the then navigable Rother, from the marauding French. It never saw any serious action, and its worst indignity was to be used for growing vegetables in the 18th century. It is nevertheless an imposing site, the archetypal moated castle, with a romantic charm that has been captured by thousands of professional and amateur photographers, and is often used as a location by filmmakers.
Population: 260.

PLACES OF INTEREST
Bodiam Castle
Tel: (058083) 436
One of the best-preserved examples of medieval moated military architecture. Built sometime between 1385 and

15

THE SUGAR-LOAF, ONE OF JACK FULLER'S FOLLIES, NEAR BRIGHTLING

1389 for protection against a French invasion that never came. Uninhabited since 17th century.

Months Open: March - October. Days Open: Every day . Hours Open: 10am - 6pm (or sunset if earlier). Admission: £1.30. Children half price. Refreshments available between March 24th till end of October.

RESTAURANT

The Walnut Tree Restaurant
Staplecross Road. Tel: (058 083) 519

PUBLIC HOUSE

The Castle Inn
Tel: (058 083) 330

CAFÉ/TEA ROOMS

Knollys Tea Rooms
Knollys. Tel: (058 083) 323

🍂 🍂 🍂 🍂 🍂 🍂 🍂

BOREHAM STREET

An elegant village lining the main road between Hailsham and Bexhill, close to Herstmonceux Castle.

RESTAURANTS

The Cellar Restaurant
Tel: (0323) 832355
The Chestnut Tree Restaurant
Tel: (0323) 833651
Smugglers Wheel
Tel: (0323) 832293

🍂 🍂 🍂 🍂 🍂 🍂 🍂

BRIGHTLING

Within the churchyard is a large pyramid containing the remains of 'Mad', (some say 'Honest') Jack Fuller, supposedly sitting in a top hat and clutching a bottle of claret. This larger-than-life figure, known as the hippopotamus, was responsible for several follies in the area; most famously the Sugar-Loaf, a cemented structure. He was also a patron of the painter, Turner. William of Wykeham, builder of much of Oxford and Winchester was rector here in 1362.

Population: 329.

PUBLIC HOUSE

Jack Fuller's
Oxley's Green. TN32 5HD Tel: (042 482) 212

THE ROYAL PAVILION, ONE OF THE MOST SPECTACULAR BUILDINGS IN THE BRITISH ISLES

BRIGHTON

On the site of the former fishing village of Bright-helmestone was born Brighton, illegitimate child of the Prince Regent's Pavilion and the railway age. (During the Industrial Revolution it grew faster than any other town in the country, Manchester included.) Like the Pavilion, the town always veers towards grandiose bad taste and an irredeemable sense of fun. Brighton sea-front is one of the most spectacular in the land. The promenade is broad and long and unbroken, from Hove in the west, right out to the new Marina. The sea front road is pink, which gives it a cosmopolitan feel, and there are fine hotels, and squares coming down to the sea. Brighton's two finest and largest hotels, the Grand and the Metropole stand side-by-side overlooking the sea, the Grand now showing no sign of wreckage of the bomb planted during the Tory party conference of 1984. The conference trade is big in Brighton, every year one of the major political party conferences are held here, in the Brighton Centre, which also hosts pop concerts, and sporting events. There are two piers, although West Pier is in a sad state of repair; the £1

it was on sale for recently would be just one of the thousands needed to refurbish it. Happily, Palace Pier further along the front remains all that good piers should be. Further east of Palace Pier is the site of the old Chain Pier, where Queen Victoria once alighted, and now where the London-Brighton Veteran Car Rally terminates every autumn. The shopping facilities around Western Road are excellent, and the Lanes are an enchanting collection of winding passages full of interesting shops, boutiques and wine bars. Brighton has evolved from a traditional English seaside holiday town into undoubtedly the premier international resort in the country.

Population: 147,336.

PLACES OF INTEREST

Booth Museum of Natural History

194 Dyke Road.

Tel: (0273) 552586

A display of British birds in settings re-creating their natural habitat. Galleries on Butterflies of the World and Sussex Geology. Reference collections of insects, osteology, palaeontology, bird and mammal skins, eggs and

17

THE GRAND HOTEL, SHOWING NO SIGN OF THE WRECKAGE OF THE BOMB PLANTED DURING THE TORY PARTY CONFERENCE OF 1984

herbaria.

Months Open: All year. Days Open: Monday - Saturday (closed Thursdays). Hours Open: Mon - Sat 10am - 5.45pm; Sunday 2 - 5pm. Bank Holidays: Closed Dec 25, 26, Jan 1 & Good Friday. Admission: Free. Frequent exhibitions.

Brighton Museum and Art Gallery

Church Street.

Tel: (0273) 603005

Includes the Willett Collection of English pottery and porcelain. Art Noveau and Art Deco, old master paintings, furniture, fashion and musical instruments.

Months Open: All year. Days Open: Tuesday - Sunday. Hours Open: 10am- 5.45pm: Sundays 2 - 5pm. Bank Holidays: Closed December 25, 26, January 1, Good Friday. Admission: Free. Frequent special exhibitions.

Brighton Railway Museum

Highcroft Villas, Preston Park.

Tel: (0273) 566151

Palace Pier

Recently tastefully renovated, it now boasts a pub and restaurant as well as the regulation tea-rooms and slot machines.

Preston Manor

Tel: (0273) 603005

Set in Preston Park off the London Road, Preston Manor was rebuilt in 1738, with further additions in 1905. Contains a notable collection of English and Continental furniture, silver, porcelain and pictures. Servants quarters now open.

Months Open: All year. Days Open: Tuesday - Sunday. Hours Open: 10am - 5pm. Garden free.

Royal Pavilion

Tel: (0273) 603005

It is hard to imagine that this extraordinary building started life as a fairly ordinary Sussex farm house rented by the Prince Regent in 1786, so that he could live near his secret bride. The Prince first commissioned Henry Holland to enlarge it, which he did by building a second farm house and joining the two by a rotunda. In 1815 John Nash was commissioned to convert it into one of the most spectacular buildings in the British Isles. The stables, known as the Dome, now house a large auditorium as well as the town library, an excellent museum and art gallery.

Months Open: All year. Days Open: Everyday. Hours Open: 10am - 5pm. Bank Holidays: Closed Christmas and Boxing Day. Tea-room. Ground floor accessible by wheelchairs.

HOTELS

Abbacourt Hotel (right)

33, Oriental Place. BN1 2LL. Tel: (0273) 25651

Delightful Regency hotel adjacent to the beach, Conference Centre, Metropole and shops. Spacious rooms with colour TV and hospitality trays. Excellent value B & B.

BEDROOMS: 3 Single, (3 TV, 3 tea/coffee) B&B £ 16.50 - £ 19.50. 4 Double, (4 TV, 4 tea/coffee) B&B £ 16.50 - £ 19.50. 2 Twin, (2 TV, 2 tea/coffee) B&B £ 16.50 - £ 19.50. 1 Family, (1 TV, 1 tea/coffee).

The Abbey Hotel

14, Norfolk Terrace. Tel: (0273) 778771

The Acropolis Hotel

14, Burlington Street. Tel: (0273) 821541

The Adelaide Hotel

51, Regency Square. Tel: (0273) 205286

Adelphi Court Hotel

19, Regency Square. Tel: (0273) 29530

Almir House Hotel

19, Sillwood Road. Tel: (0273) 25190

The Amalfi Hotel

44, Marine Parade. Tel: (0273) 607956

Ambassador Hotel

22, New Steine. Tel: (0273) 676869

Andorra Hotel

15 - 16 , Oriental Place. Tel: (0273) 21787

Annabelles Olde English Lodging House

9, Charles Street. Tel: (0273) 605845

Aquamarine Hotel

46, Kings Road. Tel: (0273) 207475

A town house hotel offering a relaxed and informal atmosphere on the seafront in front of the historic lanes.

BEDROOMS: 12 Double, (12 en suite, 12 TV, 12 phone, 12 tea/ coffee) B&B £ 50.00 - £ 68.00. 1 Four Poster £ 100.00. 1 Suite. RESTAURANT: Traditional Cuisine. HOTEL INFORMATION: CF. W. Credit Cards: Ac. Am. D. V.

Weekend Breaks: 2 nights: £ 97.50.

The Arlanda Hotel

20, New Steine. BN2 1PD. Tel: (0273) 699300

BEDROOMS: 4 Single, (4 en suite, 4 TV, 4 phone, 4 tea/coffee) B&B £ 23.00 - £ 25.00. 3 Double, (3 en suite, 3 TV, 3 phone, 3 tea/coffee) B&B £ 40.00 - £ 50.00. 5 Family, (5 en suite, 5 TV, 5 phone, 5 tea/coffee) £ 40.00–£ 50.00 Credit Cards: Ac. Am. D. V.

Arnold House Hotel

Montpelier Terrace. Tel: (0273) 25055

Ascott House

21, New Steine. Tel: (0273) 688085

Aston Hotel

3, Lower Rock Gardens. Tel: (0273) 681957

The Atlantic Hotel and Restaurant

16, Marine Parade. Tel: (0273) 695944

The Beach House Hotel

4, New Steine. Tel: (0273) 605629

Beacon Royal Hotel

ABBACOURT HOTEL

Oriental Place. Tel: (0273) 25680

Beaufort Hotel

175, Queens Park Road. Tel: (0273) 682824

Bedford Hotel

Kings Road. Tel: (0273) 29744

Brunswick Hotel

69, Brunswick Place. BN3 1NE. Tel: (0273) 733326

Byron Court Hotel

12, Grafton Street. Tel: (0273) 605035

Casa Sorrento

48, Queens Road. Tel: (0273) 25329

Cecil House Hotel

126, Kings Road. Tel: (0273) 25942

The Commodore Hotel

18, New Steine. Tel: (0273) 682124

The Cosmopolitan Hotel

31, New Steine. Tel: (0273) 682461

The Curzon Hotel

Cavendish Place. Tel: (0273) 25788

The Dove Hotel

18, Regency Square. Tel: (0273) 779222

Elgar House

3 Grafton Street, Kemptown. Tel: (0273) 695733

Ellesmere Hotel

8, New Steine. Tel: (0273) 681936

Fredellen Hotel

19, Oriental Place. Tel: (0273) 27646

Fyfield House Hotel

26, New Steine. Tel: (0273) 602770

The George Hamilton V Hotel

27, Lower Rock Gardnes. Tel: (0273) 682667

The Grand Hotel

Kings Road. Tel: (0273) 21188

Granville Hotel

125, Kings Road. Tel: (0273) 26302

Greenyards Hotel

23, New Steine. Tel: (0273) 684212

The Guernsey Hotel

34, Oriental Place. Tel: (0273) 26052

Haut Rocher Hotel

36, Upper Rock Gardens. Tel: (0273) 682939

The Hotel Metropole

Kings Road. Tel: (0273) 775432

Keehans Hotel

57, Regency Square. Tel: (0273) 207647

Kempton House Hotel

33-34, Marine Parade. BN2 1TR. Tel: (0273) 570248

BEDROOMS: 5 Double, (5 en suite, 5 TV, 5 phone, 5 tea/coffee) B&B £ 20.00 - £ 25.00. 3 Twin, (3 en suite, 3 TV, 3 phone, 3 tea/coffee) B&B £ 20.00 - £ 25.00. 4 Family, (4 en suite, 4 TV, 4 phone, 4 tea/coffee) £ 20.00–£ 25.00. 1 Four Poster. Credit Cards: Ac. Am. D. V.

Kennedy Palace Hotel

11, Marine Parade. Tel: (0273) 604928

Kimberley Hotel

17, Atlingworth Street. Tel: (0273) 603504

The Kings Arms Hotel

56, George Street. Tel: (0273) 681573

The Kings Hotel

139/141 , Kings Road. Tel: (0273) 820854

BEDROOMS: 17 Single, (17 en suite, 17 TV, 17 phone, 17 tea/coffee) 38 Double, (38 en suite, 38 TV, 38 phone, 38 tea/coffee) 27 Twin, (27 en suite, 27 TV, 27 phone, 27 tea/coffee) RESTAURANT: International Cuisine. Lunch: £ 8.50. Dinner: £ 12.50. House Wine: £ 6.75. HOTEL INFORMATION: CF. W. B. F. 10 space Car Park. Credit Cards: Ac. Am. D. V.

Weekend Breaks: 2 nights: £ 79.00. 3 nights: £ 118.50.

The Kings Palace Hotel

15, Kings Road. Tel: (0273) 26848

Kingsway Hotel

2, St Aunyns. Tel: (0273) 722068

The Lanes Hotel

71, Marine Parade. Tel: (0273) 674231

Le Flemings Hotel

12a, Regency Square. Tel: (0273) 27539

Le Flemings is a small luxurious hotel situated on Brighton sea front adjacent to Exhibition Hall and Conference Centre.

BEDROOMS: 1 Single, (1 en suite, 1 TV, 1 phone, 1 tea/coffee) B&B £ 25.00 - £ 35.00. 5 Double, (5 en suite, 5 TV, 5 phone, 5 tea/coffee) B&B £ 35.00 - £ 50.00. 3 Family, (3 en suite, 3 TV, 3

phone, 3 tea/coffee) £ 45.00–£ 60.00 .HOTEL INFORMATION: CF. Credit Cards: Ac. Am. D. V.

Weekend Breaks: 2 nights: £ 40.00. 3 nights: £ 60.00.

Lennep Hotel

57, Marine Parade. Tel: (0273) 604376

Madeira Hotel

19/23, Marine Parade. Tel: (0273) 698331

Magnolia House

274, Dyke Road. Tel: (0273) 552144

Maon Hotel

26, Upper Rock Gardens. Tel: (0273) 694400

Marina House Hotel

8, Charlotte Street. BN2 1AG. Tel: (0273) 605349/ 679484

Near sea, business & tourist centres. Cosy, well maintained & run. Hospitable, helpful, elegantly furnished & equipped, clean, comfortable. Appreciated by holiday & business visitors. Best in price range.

BEDROOMS: 3 Single, (3 TV, 3 phone, 3 tea/coffee) B&B £ 13.00 - £ 19.00. 7 Double, (7 en suite, 7 TV, 7 phone, 7 tea/coffee) B&B £ 29.00 - £ 37.00. 3 Twin, (3 en suite, 3 TV, 3 phone, 3 tea/coffee) B&B £ 31.00 - £ 48.00. 3 Family, (3 en suite, 3 TV, 3 phone, 3 tea/coffee) £ 36.00–£ 51.00 RESTAURANT: English, Chinese, Indian, vegetarian & special diet Cuisine. Lunch: £ 5.00. Tea: £ 3.00. Dinner: £ 7.00. House Wine: £ 3.00. À La Carte: £ 7.00. Specialities: Halal, Kosher. HOTEL INFORMATION: CF. W. Credit Cards: Ac. Am. D. V.

Weekend Breaks: 2 nights: £ 28.00. 3 nights: £ 39.00.

Marina West Hotel

26, Oriental Place. BN1 2LL. Tel: (0273) 23087

Marine View Hotel

24, New Steine. Tel: (0273) 603870

Marlborough Hotel

4, Princes Street. Tel: (0273) 570028

Melford Hall Hotel

41, Marine Parade. Tel: (0273) 681435

Montpelier Hall

17, Montpelier Terrace. BN1 3DF. Tel: (0273) 203599

The Montpelier Inn

Montpelier Place. Tel: (0273) 770916

New Steine Hotel

12a, New Steine. Tel: (0273) 681546

Norfolk Resort Hotel

149, Kings Road. Tel: (0273) 738201

Ocean Flatlet Hotel

11, Regency Square. Tel: (0273) 21533

The Old Ship Hotel

Kings Road. Tel: (0273) 29001

The Orient Hotel

8 / 10, Oriental Place. Tel: (0273) 25082

Oxford House Hotel

8, Pool Valley. Tel: (0273) 727689

Paskins Hotel

19, Charlotte Street. Tel: (0273) 601203

Penny Lane Hotel
11, Charlotte Street. Tel: (0273) 603197

Portland House Hotel
55/56, Regency Square. BN1 2FF. Tel: (0273) 820464

Preston Resort Hotel
216, Preston Road. Tel: (0273) 507853

The Prince Regent Hotel
29, Regency Square. Tel: (0273) 29962

Princes Hotel
Grand Junction Road. Tel: (0273) 23451

The Queens Head Hotel
69/70, Queens Road. Tel: (0273) 202476

The Queens Hotel
1 - 5, Kings Road. Tel: (0273) 21222
B&B £ 95.00 - £ 110.00. 12 Suites

The Queensbury Hotel
58, Regency Square. Tel: (0273) 25558

Ramada Renaissance Hotel
Kings Road. Tel: (0273) 206700

Regency Hotel
28, Regency Square. BN1 2FH. Tel: (0273) 202690

Regency House Hotel
29, Oriental Place. Tel: (0273) 28285

The Royal Albion Hotel
Old Steine. Tel: (0273) 29202

The Royal Crescent Hotel
100, Marine Parade. BN2 1AX. Tel: (0273) 606311

Royal Promenade Hotel
3 / 5, Percival Terrace. Tel: (0273) 675516

Russell Lodge Hotel
13, Holland Road. Tel: (0273) 770256

The Sheridan Hotel
64, Kings Road. Tel: (0273) 23171

Sillwood Lodge
6, Sillwood Place. BN1 2LH. Tel: (0273) 203985

The Skye Hotel
21, Oriental Place. Tel: (0273) 29430

Squirrels Hotel
32, Montpelier Road. Tel: (0273) 736383

St James Hotel
St James Street. Tel: (0273) 604169

Sunnyside Hotel
6, Portland Place. Tel: (0273) 605759

Sutherland Hotel
9 / 10, Regency Square. Tel: (0273) 27055

Tavistock Hotel
14, Bedford Square. Tel: (0273) 736758

Temple Court Hotel
2, Portland Place. Tel: (0273) 681241

Topps Hotel
17, Regency Square. Tel: (0273) 729334
BEDROOMS: 5 Single, (5 en suite, 5 TV, 5 phone, 5 tea/coffee) B&B £ 31.00 - £ 52.00. 5 Double, (5 en suite, 5 TV, 5 phone, 5 tea/coffee) B&B £ 52.00 - £ 65.00. 2 Twin, (2 en suite, 2 TV, 2

phone, 2 tea/coffee) B&B £ 60.00 - £ 75.00. 2 Four Posters. 2 Suites. RESTAURANT: English Cuisine. Dinner: £ 15.95. House Wine: £ 5.50.
Weekend Breaks: 2 nights: £ 52.00. 3 nights: £ 78.00.

Trouville Hotel
11, New Steine. BN2 1PB. Tel: (0273) 697384

The Twenty One Hotel
21, Charlotte Street. Tel: (0273) 686450

Wardley Hotel
10, Somerhill Avenue. Tel: (0273) 730910

Welcombe Hotel
6, Grafton Street. Tel: (0273) 604577

The Wellington Hotel
27, Waterloo Street. Tel: (0273) 23171

West Beach Hotel
135, Kings Road. Tel: (0273) 23161

West Pier Hotel
14/15, Regency Square. Tel: (0273) 28399

Wheelers Sheridan Hotel
64, Kings Road. Tel: (0273) 23221

GUEST HOUSES

Aegean Hotel
5, New Steine. Tel: (0273) 686547

Alexandra Guest House
18, Madeira Place. Tel: (0273) 681653

Almara Guest House
11, Madeira Place. Tel: (0273) 603186

Aquarium Guest House
13, Madeira Place. Tel: (0273) 605761

Argyle Guest House
21, Atlingworth Street. Tel: (0273) 685193

Ascot House
24, Russell Square. Tel: (0273) 515795

Ashley Court Guest House
33, Montpelier Road. Tel: (0273) 739916

Avalon Guest House
7, Upper Rock Gardens. Tel: (0273) 692344

Bannings Guest House
14, Upper Rock Gardens. BN2 1QE. Tel: (0273) 681403
Months Open: 12. Number of Bedrooms: 6 (2 with bathroom). TV in rooms. Pets welcome. Proprietor: G Norris.

Bensons
16, Egremont Place. Tel: (0273) 698852

Beynon House
24, St. Georges Terrace. Tel: (0273) 681014

Blades
12, Upper Rock Gardens. Tel: (0273) 694542

Bonanza Hotel
48, Queens Road . Tel: (0273) 25329

Budgies Guest house
7, Madeira Place. Tel: (0273) 683533

M. K. Cameron
8, Charles Street. Tel: (0273) 607768

Cavalaire Guest House
34, Upper Rock Gardens. Tel: (0273) 696899

Charlotte House
9, Charlotte Street. Tel: (0273) 692849

Charlton Guest House
8, Broad Street. Tel: (0273) 601489

W.W. Christie
12, Bloomsbury Place . Tel: (0273) 603967

Colson House
17, Upper Rock Gardens. Tel: (0273) 694922

Convent Of Mercy
13, Bristol Road. Tel: (0273) 607642

Court Craven Hotel
2, Atlingworth Street. Tel: (0273) 607710

Cranleigh Guest House
22, Terminus Road. Tel: (0273) 27971

Danehurst Guest House
2 & 3 Broad Street , Marine Parade. Tel: (0273) 684272

Diane House
25, St. Georges Terrace. Tel: (0273) 605797

The Dolphin Guest House
10, Charles Street. Tel: (0273) 682318

Dormuir Guest House
8, Grafton Street. Tel: (0273) 604826

Dorset Guest House
17, Dorset Gardens. Tel: (0273) 694646

Dudley House
10, Maderia Place. Tel: (0273) 676794

Elgin House
42, Russell Square. Tel: (0273) 206447

Evercliffe House Hotel
35, Upper Rock Gardens. Tel: (0273) 681161
Recently refurbished to very high standards. Majority of rooms en suite,all with colour TV, telephone, tea facilities and central heating. Close to sea and Conference Centre. *Months Open: 12. Number of Bedrooms: 11. (7 with bathroom). B&B per person: £16.00 - £23.00. TV in rooms. No pets. Evening meals if pre-booked. 3 space car park. Proprietors: Chris and Terrie Kelman*

Four Season Guest House
3, Upper Rock Gardens. Tel: (0273) 681496

Franklins
41, Regency Square. Tel: (0273) 681496

Fraser Guest House
27, St. James Avenue. Tel: (0273) 601914

Funchal
17, Madeira Place. Tel: (0273) 603975

A.L.Garner
9, Broad Street. Tel: (0273) 24310

Georjan Guest House
27, Upper Rock Gardens. Tel: (0273) 694951

Glen Muir Guest House
9, College Place. Tel: (0273) 603653

Gullivers

10, New Steine. Tel: (0273) 695415

Harveys Guest House
1, Broad Street. BN2 1TJ. Tel: (0273) 699227

Irving Home
3, Charlotte Street. Tel: (0273) 607694

Kelvin Guest House
9, Madeira Place. Tel: (0273) 603735

Kenmure Hotel
15, Burlington Street. Tel: (0273) 605774

Kenworth Guest House
18, Broad Street. Tel: (0273) 681514

La Mer
7, Marine Road. Tel: (0273) 24926

Leona House
74, Middle Street. Tel: (0273) 27309

Lynton House
14, Charlotte Street. Tel: (0273) 681854

Madeira Guest House
14, Madeira Place. Tel: (0273) 681115

K.P. Mason
12, Devonshire Place. Tel: (0273) 605889

Metfield Private Guest House
17, Charlotte Street. Tel: (0273) 606470

Miami Guest House
22, Bedford Square. Tel: (0273) 778701

Midway Guest House
44, Russell Square. Tel. (0273) 25687

Parador Guest house
35, Devonshire Place. Tel: (0273) 602025

Pebbles Guest House
8, Madeira Place. Tel: (0273) 684898

A. Phillips
5, Clarence Square. Tel: (0273) 28637

Pier View Guest House
28, New Steine. Tel: (0273) 685310

Richmond House
6, Dorset Gardens. Tel: (0273) 32779

Rockhaven
18, Lower Rock Gardens. Tel: (0273) 674681

Roslyn House
33b , St. James's Street. Tel: (0273) 681697

Rothesay Guest House
11, Broad Street. Tel: (0273) 687646

Rowland House
21, St. Georges Terrace. Tel: (0273) 603639

Russell Guest House
19, Russell Square. Tel: (0273) 27969

Ryford Private Hotel
6, New Steine. Tel: (0273) 681576

S.J. Salloumi
25, Buckingham Street. Tel: (0273) 25151

Sandpiper Guest House
11, Russell Square. Tel: (0273) 28202

Saranat Guest House

THE ROYAL CRESCENT, BRIGHTON

4, Portland Road. Tel: (0273) 770171
Sea View Boarding House
9, Clarence Square. Tel: (0273) 29954
Shalimar Guest House
23, Broad Street. Tel: (0273) 694314
Shelley's Hotel
76, Middle Street. Tel: (0273) 203967
Shirley Guest House
20, St Georges Terrace. Tel: (0273) 690862
Silver Willow Guest House
42, College Road. Tel: (0273) 694242
Sinclairs Guest House
23, Upper Rock Gardens. Tel: (0273) 600006
L. V. Smith
28, New Steine. Tel: (0273) 605310
Southdene
12, Madeira Place. Tel: (0273) 683195
Sphinx Guest House
49, Queens Road. Tel: (0273) 203231
Stanway House
19, Broad Street. Tel: (0273) 602439
Suffolk House Hotel
4, Lower Rock Gardens. Tel: (0273) 27647
Tradewinds Private Hotel

16, Egremont Place. Tel: (0273) 698852
Victoria House
40, Upper Rock Gardens. Tel: (0273) 680207
Westbourne Hotel
46, Upper Rock Gardens. Tel: (0273) 686920
Willow Guest House
37, Russell Square. Tel: (0273) 26129
York Lodge
22, Atlingworth Street. Tel: (0273) 605140

RESTAURANTS

7's Restaurant
96, St James Street. Tel: (0273) 609997
Aberdeen Steak House
27, Preston Street. Tel: (0273) 26892
Agra Tandoori
263, Ditchling Road, Five Ways. Tel: (0273) 503676
Akash Tandoori Restaurant
26, Preston Street. Tel: (0273) 24494
Al Caminetto
15, Queens Road. Tel: (0273) 29507
Al Duomo
7, Pavillion Buildings. Tel: (0273) 26761
Al Forno Restaurant

23

36, East Street. Tel: (0273) 24905

Annies Restaurant
41, Middle Street. Tel: (0273) 20251

Anthony's Restaurant
74, Preston Street. Tel: (0273) 21938

Apadana Restaurant
104, Western Road. Tel: (0273) 732397

Arcade Coffee House
15b, Imperial Arcade. Tel: (0273) 26600

The Arches
40, Beaconsfield Road. Tel: (0273) 696146

Athenian Steak and Kebab House
12, Preston Street. Tel: (0273) 28662

Bartons
7 / 8, Prince Albert Street. BN1 1HG Tel: (0273) 26128

Bexes Bistro
39, Ship Street. Tel: (0273) 202106

Billy Bunters Restaurant
133, Queens Road. Tel: (0273) 25457

The Bistro Vino
128, Western Road. Tel: (0273) 732048

The Black Chapati
12, Circus parade. Tel: (0273) 699011

The Blue Parrott
6, New Road. Tel: (0273) 739424
Mexican Cuisine. Specialities: Quesadillas & tequila.

The Blues Brothers
6, Little East Street. Tel: (0273) 735527

Brighton Bystander Fast Food Shop
1, Terminus Road. Tel: (0273) 29364

Britannia Restaurant
52, Queens Road. Tel: (0273) 27683

Browns Restaurant
3 / 4 , Duke Street. Tel: (0273) 23501

The Buttery
134, Kings Road. Tel: (0273) 27269

Cafe Boulevard
1, Chesham Road. Tel: (0273) 698396

Cafe Copenhagen
7, Western Road. Tel: (0273) 777998

Cafe de Paris
40, St James Street. Tel: (0273) 603740

Cafe Interlude
19, Bedford Street. Tel: (0273) 600388

The Capital Restaurant
48, West Street. Tel: (0273) 26383

Casalingo Restaurant
29, Preston Street. Tel: (0273) 28775

The Caspian
63, Preston Street. Tel: (0273) 29041

Ceres Healthfood Restaurant
23, Market Street. Tel: (0273) 27187

Chardonnay Restaurant
33, Chesham Road. Tel: (0273) 672733

Cheungs Chinese Restaurant
68, Queens Road. Tel: (0273) 27643

Chilka House Indian Restaurant
58, Preston Street. Tel: (0273) 27343

China Garden Restaurant
88, Preston Street. Tel: (0273) 25065

Choy's Chinese Restaurant
2, Little East Street. Tel: (0273) 25305

Churchill Steak House
25, Preston Street. Tel: (0273) 25328

Concorda Bar and Restaurant
Madeira Drive. Tel: (0273) 606460

The Continental
9 / 10, Pool Valley. Tel: (0273) 24367

Coustau's Restaurant
20, Brighton Square. Tel: (0273) 25608

The Creamery Restaurant
43, Kings Road. Tel: (0273) 25488

Cripes
7, Victoria Road. BN1 3FS Tel: (0273) 27878

Crusts Restaurant
24, Market Street. Tel: (0273) 26813

The Curry Centre
66, Queens Road. Tel: (0273) 29952

D'Arcys
49, Market Street. Tel: (0273) 25560

David's Lunch House
47, New England Road. Tel: (0273) 571718

Dee's Potato Shop
11, York Place. Tel: (0273) 695645

Deep Pan Pizza Co
28, North Street. Tel: (0273) 24208

Dickens Restaurant
Kings Road. Tel: (0273) 25877

Dig in the Ribs Restaurant
47, Preston Street. Tel: (0273) 25275

Dolce Vita Restaurant
19, Bedford Place. Tel: (0273) 737200

Dukes Restaurant
6, Dukes Lane. Tel: (0273) 25945

Elizabeth Restaurant
54, Kings Road. Tel: (0273) 26859

The Elizabethan Cottage Tandoori Restaurant
134, Old London Road. Tel: (0273) 507075

English's Oyster Bar and Seafood
29/31, East Street. Tel: (0273) 27980

Eva's Restaurant
60, Ship Street. Tel: (0273) 202376

Foggs Restaurant
5, Little Western Street. Tel: (0273) 735907
English & Continental Cuisine. Hours Open: Lunch: 12pm-2.15pm. Dinner: 7.30pm-11.00pm. Last Orders: 11.00pm. Closed Dec 25 - Jan 30. Open Sundays. Lunch: £ 9.95. House Wine: £ 5.50. Credit Cards: Ac. Am. V. Seating Capacity: 30.

Food for Thought
16, Kensington Gardens. Tel: (0273) 674919

Fortes of Brighton
1, Marine Parade. Tel: (0273) 602266

The French Connection
11, Little East Street. Tel: (0273) 23354

Fudges
127a, Kings Road. Tel: (0273) 205852

Garfunkels Restaurant
27, North Street. Tel: (0273) 29091

Gars Chinese Restaurant
19, Prince Albert Street. Tel: (0273) 21321

Genghis Khan's Mongolian Barbecue
69, St James Street. Tel: (0273) 674472

The Golden Bengal Restaurant
61, Old Steine. Tel: (0273) 26912

The Golden Girl Restaurant
10, Manchester Street. Tel: (0273) 603147

The Grecian Rooms and Silver Grill
5, Cranbourne Street. Tel: (0273) 26206

Gulistan Restaurant
16, Preston Road. Tel: (0273) 682851

Halcyon Days
72, Dyke Road. Tel: (0273) 21630

Wholefood - Vegetarian Cuisine. Specialities: Home made cakes. Hours Open: Lunch: 9am-8pm weekdays. Dinner: 10am-11pm Fri & Sat. Closed half day Monday. Open 10am-3.30pm Sundays. Lunch: £ 2.75. Dinner: £ 6.00. Seating Capacity: 26. Veg. W/chair acc. P. W.

The Harrington Hotel
71, Middle Street. Tel: (0273) 27044

Haywards
51/52, North Street. Tel: (0273) 24261

Hong Kong Gardens Take Away
138, Elm Grove. Tel: (0273) 680037

Il Bischero
48, Preston Street. Tel: (0273) 25390

Il Bistro
6, Market Street. Tel: (0273) 24584

French/Italian Cuisine. Specialities: Local seafood. Hours Open: Lunch: 12 noon. Dinner: 6pm. Closed 3pm-5.30pm. Open Sundays. House Wine: £ 3.75. Credit Cards: Ac. Am. D. V. Seating Capacity: 46. Outdoor eating. P.

Jamuna Tandoori Take Away
162, Edward Street. Tel: (0273) 609349

Karachi Tandoori
163a, Western Road. Tel: (0273) 202803

Kings Steak House
12, Kings Road. Tel: (0273) 29089

The Kingswest Boulevard
West Street. Tel: (0273) 25897

La Capannina
15, Madeira Place. Tel: (0273) 680839

La Florentina
50, Norfolk Square. Tel: (0273) 774049

La Marinade
77, St Georges Road, Kemptown. Tel: (0273) 600992

La Panzana
5, Castle Square. Tel: (0273) 723544

La Pergola Restaurant
20/21, Victoria Road. Tel: (0273) 28653

La Roma
65, Preston Street. Tel: (0273) 28955

The Latin in the Lane
10, Kings Road. Tel: (0273) 28672

The Laughing Onion
80, St Georges Road. Tel: (0273) 696555

Lazy Days Restaurant
8, East Street. Tel: (0273) 205904

Le Grandgousier French Restaurant
15, Western Street. Tel: (0273) 772005

Le Paris
15, Preston Street. Tel: (0273) 731079

Le Paysan
111, St Georges Road. Tel: (0273) 697450

Les Bouchons
85, St James Street. Tel: (0273) 683152

Lorelei Coffee Lounge
5, Union Street. Tel: (0273) 27177

Ma Cuisine
43, Sillwood Street. Tel: (0273) 729908

Mamma Mia Italian Restaurant
68/69c , Preston Street. Tel: (0273) 26823

Marco Polo's Mangolian Restaurant
77, West Street. Tel: (0273) 23605

The Marmalade Eating House
31, Western Street. Tel: (0273) 772089

McDonalds
138, London Road. Tel: (0273) 690511

McDonalds
157, Western Road. Tel: (0273) 720694

The Mediterranean Food Centre
56, Queens Road. Tel: (0273) 230239

The Meeting House
19, Meeting House Lane. Tel: (0273) 24817

Melrose Restaurant
132, Kings Road. Tel: (0273) 26520

The Mock Turtle Restaurant
4, Pool Valley. Tel: (0273) 27380

Mohammed's Tandoori Restaurant
51, George Street. Tel: (0273) 602777

The Moons Restaurant
42, Meeting House Lane. Tel: (0273) 23824

Mr Chippy Restaurant
27, Gardner Street. Tel: (0273) 688710

Mr Pickwick
2, St James's Street. Tel: (0273) 604527

Muttons Restaurant
Madeira Drive. Tel: (0273) 695430

Nash's Restaurant
32, Marine Parade. Tel: (0273) 605658

The New England Seafood Restaurant
36, New England Road. Tel: (0273) 686711

The New Hong Kong
49, Preston Street. Tel: (0273) 27788

The New Lotus
107, Dyke Road. Tel: (0273) 26336

Nooris Restaurant
70/71, Ship Street. Tel: (0273) 29405

Norfolk Resort Hotel
Kings Road. Tel: (0273) 738201

Oat Cuisine
113, St Georges Road, Kemptown. Tel: (0273) 680317

Old Mother Hubbards Restaurant
24, Preston Road. Tel: (0273) 690334

The Old Ship Restaurant
Kings Road. Tel: (0273) 29001

The Orchard Restaurant
33a, Western Street. Tel: (0273) 776618

Palmers Restaurant
15, New Road. Tel: (0273) 25648

Parthenon Restaurant
10, North Street Quadrant. Tel: (0273) 25379

Peter's Restaurant
11, Market Street. Tel: (0273) 29978

The Pickwick
77, East Street. Tel: (0273) 27433

The Pie In The Sky Restaurant
87, St. James's Street. Tel: (0273) 692087

Piero's Restaurant
30, Spring Street. Tel: (0273) 29426

The Pizza Express
22, Prince Albert Street. Tel: (0273) 23205

The Pizza Hut
81, Western Road. Tel: (0273) 27991

The Pizza Place Restaurant
7, East Street. Tel: (0273) 23108

Pizzaland
77, North Street. Tel: (0273) 21707

Pizzeria Teatro
7, New Road. Tel: (0273) 202158

Prompt Corner Restaurant
36, Montpelier Road. Tel: (0273) 736624

The Queen Anne
77, West Street. Tel: (0273) 27701

Raj Mahal Restaurant
11, Duke Street. Tel: (0273) 29517

Reflexions
7 - 8 Peltham Terrace, Lewes Road. Tel: (0273) 602333

The Regency Restaurant
131, Kings Road. Tel: (0273) 25014

Rembrandt Restaurant
51, St. Georges Road. Tel: (0273) 683252

Romano's Italian restaurant
44, Preston st. Tel: (0273) 23574

Saagar Tandoori Restaurant
17, Preston Street. Tel: (0273) 23868/26003
Specialities: Tandoori and Curry dishes. Hours Open: Lunch: 12.00-3.00. Dinner: 6.00-12.00. Last Orders: 11.45pm. Closed 3pm-6pm. Open Sundays. Credit Cards: Ac. Am. D. V. Seating Capacity: 55. Veg. P. W.

Sakarya Kebab House
81, Preston Street. Tel: (0273) 24917

Salonica Taverna
14, Madeira Drive. Tel: (0273) 604462

Samsons
25, St. Georges Road. Tel: (0273) 689073

Sarahs Restaurant
43, Churchill Square. Tel: (0273) 26920

The Scottish Steakhouse
33, Preston Street. Tel: (0273) 202708

Slims Health Food Restaurant
92, Churchill Square. Tel: (0273) 24582

Slopes Bistro, Regency Cafe
2, Southover Street. Tel: (0273) 602399

Solarium Restaurant
88, Churchill Square. Tel: (0273) 27507

Solarium Restaurant
62, Churchill Square. Tel: (0273) 26569

Spotlight Restaurant
23a, Preston Street. Tel: (0273) 25928

Stubbs of Ship Street
14, Ship Street. Tel: (0273) 204005

Sun Hall Steak House
122, Kings Road. Tel: (0273) 26037

Sussex Angus Eating House Restaurant
24, Ship Street. Tel: (0273) 28853

Swan's Restaurant
21, Norfolk Square. Tel: (0273) 721211

Swiss Restaurant & William Tell
11, Queens Road. Tel: (0273) 268665

Tandoori Curryland
2, Coombe Terrace. Tel: (0273) 681280

Taverna Sorrentina
44/45, Kings Road. Tel: (0273) 25229

Themes Restaurant
13, Boyces Street. Tel: (0273) 25195

Toques Restaurant
41, Castle Street. Tel: (0273) 734987

Trogs Restaurant
125, King's Road. Tel: (0273) 733516

The Tropical Curryland Indian Restaurant
37, Ditching Road. Tel: (0273) 698554

The Tureen
31, Upper North Street. Tel: (0273) 28939

Uncle Sams Hamburger Express
47, West Street. Tel: (0273) 272406

Unit 12
25, Ditchling Rise. Tel: (0273) 681681

Vesuvio Restaurant
25, Middle Street. Tel: (0273) 27984

The Viceroy Of India
13, Preston Street. Tel: (0273) 24733

Villa Bianca
101, Western Road. Tel: (0273) 779015

The Vineyard Restaurant
64, Preston Street. Tel: (0273) 21681

Water Margin Chinese Restaurant
39, Ship Street. Tel: (0273) 21642

The Waters Edge Coffee Shop
Brighton Marina. Tel: (0273) 609657

Wheeler's Restaurant
64, Kings Road. Tel: (0273) 28372

Wheeler's Three Little Rooms Restaurant
17, Market Street.. Tel: (0273) 25135/27940

Wild Oats
12, Sidney Street. Tel: (0273) 571363

Willetts Supper Club
19, Bedford Street. Tel: (0273) 600388

Wimpy Restaurant
66, East Street. Tel: (0273) 21595

Windsor House Restaurant
28, Baker Street. Tel: (0273) 609408

Wyborn's Restaurant
97, St. James's Street. Tel: (0273) 693498

PUBLIC HOUSES

The Admiral Napier
2 Elm Grove. Tel: (0273) 605827

The Aquarium Inn
6 Steine Street. Tel: (0273) 605825

The Barley Mow
92 St Georges Road. Tel: (0273) 682559

The Basketmakers Arms
12 Gloucester Road. Tel: (0273) 689006

The Bat & Ball
51 Ditchling Road. Tel: (0273) 683887

The Bath Arms
The Lanes. Tel: (0273) 29437

The Battle Of Trafalgar
34 Guildford Road. Tel: (0273) 27997

The Battle Of Waterloo
6 Rock Place. Tel: (0273) 601139

The Beckets Head
11 Boyces Street. Tel: (0273) 25850

The Bedford Tavern
30 Western Street. Tel: (0273) 739495

The Belle Vue Inn
Buckingham Place. Tel: (0273) 28820

The Belvedere Beach Bar
159 Kings Road Arches. Tel: (0273) 25243

Bevendean Hotel
Hillside. Tel: (0273) 607246

The Black Horse
16 Montague Place. Tel: (0273) 601026

The Black Horse
112 Church Street. Tel: (0273) 606864

The Branch Tavern
London Road. Tel: (0273) 688180

The Brighton Rock
62 West Street. Tel: (0273) 28911

The Brighton Tavern
100 Gloucester Road. Tel: (0273) 680365

Bristol Bar
Paston Place. Tel: (0273) 605687

The Bugle Inn
24 Street, Martin Street. Tel: (0273) 607753

The Bulldog Tavern
31 St. James Street. Tel: (0273) 684097

The Bush
1 Arundel Road. Tel: (0273) 682159

The Chequers Inn
45 Preston Street. Tel: (0273) 29922

The Clyde Arms
Bristol Gardens. Tel: (0273) 682640

The Coachmakers Arms
76 Trafalgar Street. Tel: (0273) 695146

The Cobden Arms
45 Cobden Road. Tel: (0273) 682540

The Cock & Bottle
5 Pelham Terrace, Lewis Road. Tel: (0273) 603901

Colonnade Public House
10 New Road. Tel: (0273) 28728

The Compton Arms
82 Dyke Road. Tel: (0273) 26803

Constant Service
96 Islingword Road. Tel: (0273) 607058

The Counting House
106 Lewes Road. Tel: (0273) 684631
Once described as the best pub in Lewes it offers a selection of real ales, good food and comfort.
Free House. Opening Hours: 11.00-2.30/5.30-11.00. Beer available: Varied selection of real ales. Traditional games: Darts, pool.

The County Oak
Oak Avenue. Tel: (0273) 507584

The Cranbourne Arms
Cranbourne Street. Tel: (0273) 28447

The Cricketers Hotel
15 Black Lion Street. Tel: (0273) 49472
Brewery: Phoenix. OPEN ALL DAY. Opening Hours: 11am-11pm. Beer available: Festival, Ruddles, Websters, Holsten, Guinness. Food Available: All bar hours.

The Crown & Anchor

213 Preston Road. Tel: (0273) 509191
Cuthbert Hotel
136 Freshfield Road. Tel: (0273) 680673
The Deryk Carver
Black Lion Street. Tel: (0273) 202766
Doctor Brightons
16 / 17 Kings Road. Tel: (0273) 28765
The Dorset Arms
North Road. Tel: (0273) 605423
The Dover Castle
43 Southover Street. Tel: (0273) 605492
The Druids Arms
81 Ditchling Road. Tel: (0273) 605689
The Druids Head
9 Brighton Place. Tel: (0273) 25490
The Duke Of Wellington
Upper Gloucester Road. Tel: (0273) 27989
The Dyke Inn
218 Dyke Road. Tel: (0273) 557145
The Eastern Hotel
Eastern Road. Tel: (0273) 601618
Edinburgh Hotel
67a Upper Gloucester Road. Tel: (0273) 27075
Elephant & Castle
113 London Road. Tel: (0273) 681360
The Evening Star Inn
55 Surrey street. Tel: (0273) 28931
The Fortune Of War
157 Kings Road Arches. Tel: (0273) 21328
The Free Butts
25 Albion Street. Tel: (0273) 697221
The Freshfield Inn
Freshfield Road. Tel: (0273) 604829
The Full Moon
8 Boyces Street. Tel: (0273) 28797
Gatsbys
Grand Parade. Tel: (0273) 681228
The Gladstone Arms
123 Lewes Road. Tel: (0273) 603585
The Golden Cannon
21 St. Georges Road. Tel: (0273) 607544
The Golden Cross
16 Southover Street. Tel: (0273) 607755
The Golden Fleece Hotel
Market Street. Tel: (0273) 29483
The Great Eastern
103 Trafalgar Street. Tel: (0273) 685621
Good beer, good food, good company.
Brewery: Phoenix. OPEN ALL DAY. Sunday opening Hours:
12.00-3.00/7.00-10.30 . Beer available: Ruddles County, King &
Barnes, Holsten Export, Fosters. Food Available: 12.00-3.00.
Traditional games: Cribbage, chess, Pass the Pig.
The Green Dragon
8 Sidney Street. Tel: (0273) 607922

The Greys
105 Southover Street. Tel: (0273) 680734
The Hampton
57 Upper Street. Tel: (0273) 25425
The Hanbury Arms
83 St. Georges Road. Tel: (0273) 605789
The Hand In Hand
33 Upper Street. Tel: (0273) 602521
The Hartington
41 Whippingham Road. Tel: (0273) 682874
The Hikers Rest
Coldean Lane. Tel: (0273) 570277
The Hollingbury
1 Roedale Road. Tel: (0273) 555858
The Holsten Bar
13 Kensington Gardens. Tel: (0273) 681907
The Horse & Groom
129, Islington Road. Tel: (0273) 680696
The Jolly Brewers
176, Ditchling Road. Tel: (0273) 500295
The King & Queen
13, Marlborough Place. Tel: (0273) 607202
The London Unity
131 Islington Road. Tel: (0273) 681722
Lord Nelson
36, Trafalgar Street. Tel: (0273) 682150
The Marine Tavern
13, Broad Street. Tel: (0273) 681284
The Marquess Of Exeter
28, Hamilton Road. Tel: (0273) 556708
The Martha Gunns
Upper Lewes Road. Tel: (0273) 681671
The Mitre Tavern
13, Baker street. Tel: (0273) 413404
The Montreal Arms
62, Albion Road. Tel: (0273) 607790
The Nellie Peck
57, West Street. Tel: (0273) 26369
The New Heart In Hand
80, East Street. Tel: (0273) 204729
The Newmarket Arms
32, Bear Road. Tel: (0273) 688245
Nightingale Theatre Public House
29, Surrey Street. Tel: (0273) 29086
Nobles Bar
25, New Road. Tel: (0273) 682401
The Northern Hotel
31, York Place. Tel: (0273) 602519
The Old Vic
Ship Street. Tel: (0273) 24744
The Oriental
5, Montpelier Road. Tel: (0273) 728808
P.G.'s
1 Clarence Gardens. Tel: (0273) 27335

A lively town centre pub, ideal for shoppers and workers alike. Very popular with younger people in the evening. *Brewery: Phoenix. OPEN ALL DAY. Opening Hours: 10.30am-11.00pm. Beer available: Webster's, Ruddles, Watney's Special, Foster's, Budweiser, Holsten. Food Available: 12.00-3.00. Garden.*

Park Crescent Inn
39, Park Crescent Terrace. Tel: (0273) 720641

The Park View
Preston Drove. Tel: (0273) 604993

Pedestrian Arms
13, Foundry Street. Tel: (0273) 697014
Brewery: Phoenix. OPEN ALL DAY. Beer available: Real ales and international lagers. Food Available: 12.00-2.30. Traditional games: Pool, darts.

The Preston Brewery Tap
197, Preston Road. Tel: (0273) 508700

Preston Park Tavern
88, Havelock Road. Tel: (0273) 502418

Prestonville Arms
64, Hamilton Road. Tel: (0273) 505323

Prince Arthur
Dean street. Tel: (0273) 25531

Prince George
5, Trafalgar Street. Tel: (0273) 681055

Prince Of Victoria
22, Upper North Street. Tel: (0273) 25491

Prince Of Wales
47, Clarence Square. Tel: (0273) 24685

The Pump House
46, Market Street. Tel: (0273) 26864

The Quadrant Hotel
12, Quadrant. Tel: (0273) 26432

The Queen Victoria
54, High Street. Tel: (0273) 302121

The Queens Arms
7, George Street. Tel: (0273) 602939

The Queens Head
3a, Steine Street. Tel: (0273) 682725

The Queens Park Tavern
Queens Park Road. Tel: (0273) 682080

The Queensbury Arms
Queensbury Mews. Tel: (0273) 28159

Race Hill Inn
Lewes Road. Tel: (0273) 603819

Race Horse Inn
Elm Grove. Tel: (0273) 686030

The Railway Bell
Surrey Street. Tel: (0273) 26730

The Railway Hotel
76, Ditchling Rise. Tel: (0273) 681651

The Ranelagh Arms
2 / 3, High Street. Tel: (0273) 681634

The Red Lion

33 Up Park Place. Tel: (0273) 682373

Reflections
728 Pelham Terrace, Lewes Road. Tel: (0273) 602333

The Regency Tavern
34, Russell Square. Tel: (0273) 25652

Retreat Bar
135, Western Road. Tel: (0273) 27511

The Richmond Hotel
Richmond Place. Tel: (0273) 603974

Rockingham Inn
24, Sillwood Street. Tel: (0273) 776961

Rollers
158, Lewes Road. Tel: (0273) 602995

Rosehill Tavern
Rosehill Terrace. Tel: (0273) 607825

Roundhill Tavern
100, Ditching Road. Tel: (0273) 697497

The Royal Escape
10, Marine Parade. Tel: (0273) 606906

The Royal Exchange Inn
58, Southover Street. Tel: (0273) 601419

The Royal Oak
46, St. James's Street. Tel: (0273) 606538

The Royal Pavilion Tavern
Castle Square. Tel: (0273) 25684

The Royal Sovereign
66, Preston Street. Tel: (0273) 23289
Brewery: Phoenix. Beer available: Ruddles, Yorkshire, King & Barns.

Shakespeare's Head
1, Chatham Place. Tel: (0273) 25192

Sir Charles Napier
50, Southover Street. Tel: (0273) 601413

The Snipe Inn
Carden Avenue. Tel: (0273) 556423

The Spotted Dog
13, Middle Street. Tel: (0273) 26503

The Spread Eagle
20, Albion Hill. Tel: (0273) 686049

Springfield Hotel
146, Springfield Road. Tel: (0273) 552166

The Stable
Albion Street. Tel: (0273) 605235

The Stags Inn
33, Upper Bedford Street. Tel: (0273) 609676

Stanford Arms
2, Preston Road. Tel: (0273) 604542

Stanmer Park Hotel
Ditchling Road. Tel: (0273) 552005

The Star Inn
Manchester Street. Tel: (0273) 601450

The Station Hotel
1, Hampstead Road. Tel: (0273) 501318

Sudeley Arms

Sudeley Street. Tel: (0273) 682991

The Sussex
East Street. Tel: (0273) 27591

The Sussex Yeoman
7 Guildford Roasd. Tel: (0273) 27985

The Sutherland Arms
Sutherland Road. Tel: (0273) 27985

Temple Bar
121, Western Road. Tel: (0273) 711587

Three Jolly Butchers
59, North Street. Tel: (0273) 602688

The Thurlow Arms
161, Edward Street. Tel: (0273) 601148

The Toby Jug Inn
Cowley Drive. Tel: (0273) 304100

The Victory Inn
6, Duke Street. Tel: (0273) 26555

Volks Tavern
3 The Collanade, Madeira Drive. Tel: (0273) 682828

The Volunteer Inn
1, Church Street. Tel: (0273) 684951

The Waggon & Horses
10, Church Street. Tel: (0273) 602752

Walmer Castle
95, Queens Park Road. Tel: (0273) 682466

The Wellington
Elm Grove. Tel: (0273) 603675

The Whippet Inn
8, Queens Road. Tel: (0273) 26209

The White Admiral
Taunton Road. Tel: (0273) 607945

The White Horse Inn
Camelford Street. Tel: (0273) 682288

Whitehawk Inn
Whitehawk Road. Tel: (0273) 684510

William IV
4, Church Street. Tel: (0273) 683365

Windsor Tavern
46, Windsor Street. Tel: (0273) 26095

The Winner
291, Elm Grove. Tel: (0273) 699907

Woody's Bar & Nightspot
77/78, Middle Street. Tel: (0273) 24891

CAFÉS & TEA ROOMS

Bee's Tea's
186 Kings Road Arches. Tel: (0273) 21393

Billabong
34 Hampton Place. Tel: (0273) 774386

Bites
31 Ship Street. Tel: (0273) 571718

Bleriot
146-147 Kings Road. Tel: (0273) 821409

Brighton Chocolate House

16 Market Street. Tel: (0273) 27417

Burke J.
90 Dyke Road. Tel: (0273) 28611

Cafe Royale
50 Preston Street. Tel: (0273) 202603

The Chalet Cafe
Preston Park. Tel: (0273) 503477

Corner Cafe
30 North Road. Tel: (0273) 681361

Dallas Cafeteria
30 York Place. Tel: (0273) 682177

Derbys
39 Bond Street. Tel: (0273) 28855

Devalls Cafe
3 Terminus Road. Tel: (0273) 28861

Dials Cafe
115 Dyke Road. Tel: (0273) 28858

Digby's
10a Kensington Arcade, Kensington Gardens.
Tel: (0273) 673214

Dooks Coffee House
22, North Street. Tel: (0273) 674209

The Dumb Waiter
28, Sydney Road. Tel: (0273) 602526

Egremont Cafe
32, Egremont Place. Tel: (0273) 683262

Elm Grove Cafe
89, Elm Grove. Tel: (0273) 698394

Ernie's Cafe
15, Coombe Terrace. Tel: (0273) 681808

Family Diner
Madeira Drive. Tel: (0273) 682132

Fan Like Fanny's
32, Preston Street. Tel: (0273) 26951

Fiji Cafe
2, Ship Street. Tel: (0273) 202629

Food Peddlers
24, Surrey Street. Tel: (0273) 205167

Gina's Cafe
11, Coombe Road. Tel: (0273) 699826

The Gravy Train
3 - 4, East Street. Tel: (0273) 202591

The Hot Potato
71, St. James's Street. Tel: (0273) 601598

J. C. Hunt
106, Upper Lewes Road. Tel: (0273) 682905

J.J.'s
3 Beaconsfield Parade, Beaconsfield Road.
Tel: (0273) 556526

Jackson Brown
53, Preston Street. Tel: (0273) 25078

John's Diner
41, New Englands Road. Tel: (0273) 681689

Kensington Cafe Shop

1, Kensington Gardens. Tel: (0273) 570963
Kitchen Cafe
93, Trafalgar Street. Tel: (0273) 602526
Le Cafe Creme
110, Church Street. Tel: (0273) 606424
Le Kiosk
Lower Esplanade Boundary Beach, Kings Road. Tel: (0273) 203891
Lewes Road Cafe
3, Lewes Road. Tel: (0273) 692794
Mac's Cafe
30, Arundel Road. Tel: (0273) 692621
Market Cafe
19, Circus Street. Tel: (0273) 608273
The Market Cafe
17 Open Market, Marshalls Row, London Road. Tel: (0273) 670351
Mrs Beeton Cafe
95, Gloucester Road. Tel: (0273) 692912
Munchies
120, St. James Street. Tel: (0273) 601990
Mustard & Pickle
9, Hampton Place. Tel: (0273) 731497
New England Soda Fountain
157, Western Road. Tel: (0273) 732665
Papa's Cafe
8, Oxford Street. Tel: (0273) 699017
Partners Coffee Shop
32, Preston Street. Tel: (0273) 26951
Pavilion Gardens Cafe
Royal Pavilion Grounds. Tel: (0273) 730712
Peggy's Snack bar
128b , Queens Road. Tel: (0273) 25278
The Piece Of Cake
53, Preston Street. Tel: (0273) 25078
Plumps Coffee Shop
32, Preston Street. Tel: (0273) 23365
Preston Street Diner
82, Preston Street. Tel: (0273) 732227
F. Robins
6, Trafalgar Street. Tel: (0273) 683766
Rotunda Cafe
Preston Park. Tel: (0273) 555460
Seaspray Snack Bar
8, Grand Parade. Tel: (0273) 37732
St. Anns Well Garden Cafe
Furze Hill , Furze Croft. Tel: (0273) 773134
The Stage Door Cafe
42, Sydney Street. Tel: (0273) 685727
Stanmer Stores
Stanmer Village . Tel: (0273) 604041
Sue's Snacks
62, Queens Road. Tel: (0273) 21982
Supersnack

7, Bond Street. Tel: (0273) 23055
Tasties
176, Edward Street. Tel: (0273) 570392
Tivoli Cafe
Madeira Drive. Tel: (0273) 606547
Top Ten Snack Bar
35 Upper Street , St.James Street. Tel: (0273) 604935
The Upstairs Cafe
Municipal Market , Circus Street. Tel: (0273) 676530
The Waddington S. Kiosk
Dyke Road Avenue. Tel: (0273) 556681
Wells Betty Beach Cafe
Madeira Drive. Tel: (0273) 681943
Whitecliffs Beach Cafe
Marine Drive. Tel: (0273) 309219
Zerbs
21, Gardner Street. Tel: (0273) 685248

OTHER AMENITIES

ART GALLERIES
Black Lion Gallery
3 Black Lion Lane. Tel: (0273) 203352
Clairmonte Galleries
12 Black Lion Lane. Tel: (0273) 203843
Florentine Galleries
14 Brighton Square. Tel: (0273) 23730
Hugo Barclay Art Gallery
7 East Street. Tel: (0273) 21694
G. F. Hussey
4 George Street. Tel: (0273) 681852
Nexus Gallery
14 Broad Street. Tel: (0273) 684480
M.A. Oxley
6 Sandgate Road. Tel: (0273) 541739
Surrounds Picture Framing
8 Little East Street. Tel: (0273) 27843
R.P. Vernon-Ward
Denehurst , Sunnydale Avenue. Tel: (0273) 502097
Window Gallery
3 Dukes Lane. Tel: (0273) 726190

BOAT HIRE
P. G. Hayles
35 Rushworth Homes , Brighton Marina. Tel: (0273) 689528
Sunsports Hire Base
185 Kings Road Arches. Tel: (0273) 23160

BUS & COACH SERVICES
Brighton Borough Transport
Coombe Terrace, Lewes Road. Tel: (0273) 606141
Bus and coach services
Months Open: Jan-Dec. Days Open: Mon-Sun. Hours Open:
8.30-5.30 9.30-5.30 Sun. Open Bank Holidays. Bus services in

and around Brighton, Hove and Lewes. Coach tours and holidays. Special 'open topper' bus tours in the summer months. National Express tickets.

National Express
178 West Street. Tel: (0273) 673237

Sussex Leamland Ltd.
20, Church Square. Tel: (0273) 721962

CAR HIRE

A. A. V. Self Drive
24, Coombe Road. Tel: (0273) 683758

Ace Radio Cars
15a , Duke Street. Tel: (0273) 721048

Albany Chauffeur Cars
43, Longhill Road. Tel: (0273) 35815

Alternative Vehicle Hire
Tel: (0273) 207373

Avis Rent-A-Car
Bedford Hotel , Kings Road. Tel: (0273) 820058

Britannia
3 - 4 , Ann Street. Tel: (0273) 570044

Budget Rent A Car
87, Preston Street. Tel: (0273) 27351

Caffyns
Dyke Road. Tel: (0273) 553061

Collins P. J. (Chauffeur-driven Volvos)
7, Nevill Close. Tel: (0273) 502323

L. D. Craig
E7 Marine Gate. Tel: (0273) 680029

Endeavour Rent-A-car
Pool Valley. Tel: (0273) 28102

Europcar
Russell Road , Cannon Place. Tel: (0273) 29332

Happy Bride Wedding Shop
138, Western Road. Tel: (0273) 25929

Lee Motors Car Hire
Church Place. Tel: (0273) 683344/300369

Plan-It Car Hire
154, Bevendean Crescent. Tel: (0273) 601346

P. S. Scrase
28, Brangwyn Avenue. Tel: (0273) 682484

Swan National
Cannon Place. Tel: (0273) 202426

Villa Cars
34, Ship Street. Tel: (0273) 205025

Walker's Car Hire
210, Ditchling Road. Tel: (0273) 500600

Whitegift Hire
British Rail Gardens Yard, Cheapside. Tel: (0273) 697374

CARAVAN PARK

Caravan Club
Brighton Race Course. Tel: (0273) 692964

CINEMAS

Duke of York's Cinema
Preston Circus. Tel: (0273) 602503

Odeon Theatres
Kings West House, West Street. Tel: (0273) 25890

GARDEN CENTRES

Cramphorn Plc
54, London Road. Tel: (0273) 603699

Eastwoods Town Centre Garden Centre
235, Ditching Road . Tel: (0273) 505058

HEALTH CLUBS

Ace Gym & Fitness Centre
5-8, Dukes Court Street. Tel: (0273) 29939

Brighton Judo & Karate Centre
21, Vine Street. Tel: (0273) 683633

Brighton Natural Health Centre
27, Regent Street. Tel: (0273) 600010
Educational charity for the promotion of natural health Months Open: Jan-Dec. Days Open: Mon-Fri. Hours Open: 10am - 3pm. Not open on Bank Holidays. The Natural Health Centre is a registered educational charity for the promotion of natural health in the community and specialises in courses on natural health. Courses can be daytime, evening or weekend. Rates: Annual membership £12. Proprietor: Mr Jeddi Bassan

Bristol Gardens Health Spa
24 Bristol Gardens. Tel: (0273) 698904

Edens Saunasium
75, Grand Parade. Tel: (0273) 682031

The Fitness Factory
24, Castle Street. Tel: (0273) 775749

Heatwave Suntan Studios
36, Meeting House Lane. Tel: (0273) 26613

J. C.'s Bodybuilding Energy Store, Exercise & Dance Studio
10, Gloucester Place. Tel: (0273) 605495

John Carr's Gym
18b , Margaret Street. Tel: (0273) 690252

Julia Swift Exercise
Old Slipper Baths , North Road. Tel: (0273) 690016

Manorbe Health Studio
121, Western Road. Tel: (0273) 737954

Shape Health Studios
38, Devonshire Place. Tel: (0273) 608617

The Surrey Diet Centre
Planet House, 65 Church Road. Tel: (0273) 24860

The Time Out Club
130, Queens Road. Tel: (0273) 770824

HOSPITALS

Royal Alexandra Hospital
Dyke Road. Tel: (0273) 2814528148

Royal Sussex County Hospital

Royal York Buildings, Old Steine. Tel: (0273) 728486
Sussex Eye Hospital
Eastern Road. Tel: (0273) 606126
Sussex Nuffield Hospital
55, New Church Road. Tel: (0273) 779471/774443

HOSTELS
Hillel House Student Hostel
18 Harrington Road. Tel: (0273) 503450
Young Mens Christian Association
50 Old Steine. Tel: (0273) 206161
Youth Hostels Association
Patcham Place. Tel: (0273) 556196

LEISURE CENTRES
Big Country Water Slides UK
22, Richmond Place. Tel: (0273) 570940
Wilsons Leisure
6, York Place. Tel: (0273) 688734

NIGHT CLUBS
Club Savannah
32, Old Steine. Tel: (0273) 681800
Keeler Club
49, Gloucester Road. Tel: (0273) 673674
Kings West
Kings West Boulevard, West Street. Tel: (0273) 732627
Melons Nite Spot
214/215 , Kings Road Arches. Tel: (0273) 202807
Monroes
37, West Street. Tel: (0273) 21692
Monti's
21, Montpelier Road. Tel: (0273) 774141
New Zorba's Taverna
75a , West Street. Tel: (0273) 24381
Queens Night Club
1 - 5 , Kings Road. Tel: (0273) 21222
Secrets Club
25, Steine Street. Tel: (0273) 609672
Shades Night Club
Castle Square. Tel: (0273) 29451
Zap Club
191/193 , Kings Road Arches. Tel: (0273) 775987

RAILWAY STATION
Brighton Station
Queens Road. Tel: (0273) 25476

SAUNAS
The Design Centre Solarium
124, Elm Grove. Tel: (0273) 605983
Edens Saunasium
75, Grand Parade. Tel: (0273) 682031

Factor 1 Solarium
42, Preston Street. Tel: (0273) 207509

SKATING RINK
Sussex Ice Rink
11, Queen Square. Tel: (0273) 24677

SNOOKER CENTRE
Castle Snooker Club
22-23 , Castle Street. Tel: (0273) 775703

STORES
BHS Plc
12, Western Road. Tel: (0273) 24383
J. Blundell
8, Kensington Gardens. Tel: (0273) 570150
Brighton Co-Operative Society Ltd
94/101 , London Road. Tel: (0273) 606722
Debenhams Plc.
95/99 , Western Road. Tel: (0273) 26531
Hanningtons Ltd
North Street. Tel: (0273) 29877
Marks & Spencer Plc.
195, Western Road. Tel: (0273) 28081
Peacock Stores Ltd.
Unit 5, 5 - 8 London Road. Tel: (0273) 571547
Primark Stores Ltd.
188, Western Road. Tel: (0273) 205211
Vokins
North Street. Tel: (0273) 23211
Woolworths Plc
185, Western Road. Tel: (0273) 29262/203067

SWIMMING POOLS
St. Luke's Pool
St. Luke's Terrace . Tel: (0273) 602385
Surrenden Swimming Pool
Surrenden Road. Tel: (0273) 504858

TAXIS
Ace Taxis
15a Duke Street. Tel: (0273) 27000
Brighton & Hove Radio Cabs
31a Bath Street. Tel: (0273) 24245
Brotax Private Hire
14 Southover Street. Tel: (0273) 681593
Mercury Cabs
77 Preston Street. Tel: (0273) 26433
Southern Taxis (Brighton) Ltd
63 Queens Road. BN1 3XD Tel: (0273) 24555
Taxi agency
Months Open: 12 months per year.
Days Open: 7 days per week.

Hours Open: 24 hours per day. Open all Bank Holidays.
Proprietor: Mr D K Banks.
Streamline Taxis
5 Clifton Hill. Tel: (0273) 729402

THEATRES
Brighton Actors Theatre
The Nightingale, 29 Surrey Street. Tel: (0273) 26786
Brighton Dome Complex
29 New Road. Tel: (0273) 685097/674357
Theatre Royal
New Road. Tel: (0273) 28488

TOURS & SIGHTS
Brighton Coaches
43-45 Coombe Terrace, Lewes Road. Tel: (0273) 606141
St. Georges Travel Service
26 St. Georges Road. Tel: (0273) 685371

WATER SPORTS
Leisure Themes Marketing Ltd.
22 Richmond Place. Tel: (0273) 570233
Sunsports Watersports Centre
91 Preston Street. Tel: (0273) 28584

WINE BARS
Beckets Bar
20 Preston Street . Tel: (0273) 26408
Kings Wine Bar
15a Kings Road. Tel: (0273) 28290
Naysmiths Wine Bar
59 Queens Road. Tel: (0273) 820305
Pharoah's
23 Old Steine . Tel: (0273) 605734

⅋ ⅋ ⅋ ⅋ ⅋ ⅋ ⅋

BROAD OAK
This little village stands on a crossroads in the hilly wooded countryside north of Hastings.

PUBLIC HOUSE
The Rainbow Trout
Tel: (0424) 882436

⅋ ⅋ ⅋ ⅋ ⅋ ⅋ ⅋

BROADOAK
A tiny village between Heathfield and Burwash.

OTHER AMENITIES
CAR HIRE/SELF DRIVE
Broad Oak Garage
Burwash Road. Tel: (043 52) 5577

GARDEN CENTRE
Old Barklye Nurseries
Swife Lane. Tel: (0435) 883258

⅋ ⅋ ⅋ ⅋ ⅋ ⅋ ⅋

BURWASH
The wooded hills around and about inspired Burwash's most famous resident, Rudyard Kipling, to write 'Puck of Pook's Hill', based on tales told him by an old Sussex woodsman. Five miles east of Heathfield, the village has a single main street with a beautiful collection of houses and cottages, with the church of St. Bartholemew at the eastern extreme. In the summer it does become somewhat overrun by tourists visiting Batemans.
Population: 2,304.

PLACES OF INTEREST
Batemans
Tel: (0435) 882302
Rudyard Kipling's home between 1902-36, where his study remains as it was in his lifetime, and his Rolls-Royce is still in the garage. Nearby is the hill, now recorded as Perch Hill, that featured in Puck of Pooks Hill. Alongside the house is an old mill.
Months Open: April-October. Days Open: Everyday, except Thursday and Friday. Hours Open: 11am-6pm. Admission: £2.80. Light lunches and tea in tea-room, picknicking in Quarry Garden.

HOTELS
The Admiral Vernon Inn
High Street. Tel: (0435) 882230
The Bear Inn and Burwash Motel
High Street. Tel: (0435) 882540
Situated in the midst of an area of outstanding beauty, this delightful beamed bar/restaurant has been extended to provide superb motel units.
BEDROOMS: 4 Double, (4 en suite, 4 TV, 4 phone, 4 tea/coffee) B&B £ 29.00 - £ 43.00. 4 Twin, (4 en suite, 4 TV, 4 phone, 4 tea/ coffee) B&B £ 29.00 - £ 43.00. RESTAURANT: Traditional Cuisine. Lunch: £ 5.00. Tea: £ 3.00. Dinner: £ 10.00. House Wine: £ 5.95. À La Carte: £ 7.50. HOTEL INFORMATION: CF. W. B. F. 100 space Car Park. Dogs. Credit Cards: Ac. Am.
Bell Inn
High Street. Tel: (0435) 882304
The Kicking Donkey Inn
Witherenden Hill. Tel: (0435) 883379

RESTAURANT
Tudor House Restaurant
High Street. Tel: (0435) 882258

BATEMANS, RUDYARD KIPLING'S HOME FROM 1902-36

PUBLIC HOUSE
Rose & Crown Inn
Ham Lane. Tel: (0435) 882600

OTHER AMENITIES
FISH FARM
Lakedown Trout Fisheries
Witherenden Hill. Tel: (0435) 883449

TAXI
Pookshill Cars
Puck's Hill, Heathfield Road. Tel: (0435) 882751

🐾 🐾 🐾 🐾 🐾 🐾 🐾

BURWASH COMMON
A small village on the A 256 two and a quarter miles west of Burwash itself, with a Victorian church.

OTHER AMENITY
GARDEN CENTRE
K.R. Shanks
Old Orchard Nursery, Heathfield Road (A265). Tel: (0435) 882060

🐾 🐾 🐾 🐾 🐾 🐾 🐾

BURWASH WEALD
Lying between Burwash and Burwash Common.

PUBLIC HOUSE
The Wheel Inn
Tel: (0435) 882758

OTHER AMENITY
TAXI
Burwash Weald Taxis
Weland, Willingford Lane. Tel: (0435) 882772

🐾 🐾 🐾 🐾 🐾 🐾 🐾

BUXTED
The village was removed from its original site around the church by Lord Liverpool, jealous of his privacy, when he came into possession of Buxted Park in the 1830s. The church, now isolated, is unusually dedicated to St. Margaret, an 11th century queen of Scotland. William Wordsworth's brother, a former rector, is buried in the churchyard.
Population: 3,888.

HOTELS
Buxted Inn
High Street. Tel: (082 581) 3510
Buxted Park
Tel: (082 581) 2711

OTHER AMENITY
HEALTH CLUB
Buxted Park
Buxted Park. TN22 4AY Tel: (082 581) 2711

🐾 🐾 🐾 🐾 🐾 🐾 🐾

CAMBER
A holiday village built among the sand-dunes between Rye and the atomic power station at Dungeness, on the edge of Romney Marsh. The most easterly settlement in the county.
Population: 718.

HOTELS
Cinque Ports Lodge Hotel
93 Lydd Road. Tel: (0797) 225073
Situated adjacent to the superb Camber beach and only five minutes by road from the ancient Cinque Port of Rye.
*BEDROOMS: 5 Double, (5 en suite, 5 TV, 5 phone,) B&B £18.00 - £25.00. 2 Twin, (2 en suite, 2 TV, 2 phone,) 2 Family, (2 en suite, 2 TV, 2 phone,) RESTAURANT: Tea: £2.50. Dinner: £5.00. House Wine: £5.50. HOTEL INFORMATION: CF. W. Credit Cards: Ac. Recommendations: AA****.*
The Green Owl Hotel
11 Old Lydd Road. Tel: (0797) 225284
Royal William Hotel
Old Lydd Road. Tel: (0797) 225231

RESTAURANTS
Bermudan Fish & Chip Shop
Old Lydd Road. Tel: (0797) 225352
Coach House Restaurant
100 Lydd Road. Tel: (0797) 225342
Eel Bar
New Lydd Road. Tel: (0797) 226025

PUBLIC HOUSE
Camber Castle
Lydd Road. Tel: (0797) 225429 / 225313

CAFÉ/TEA ROOMS
New Marine Cafe
Central Car Park, Old Lydd Road. Tel: (0797) 224358

OTHER AMENITIES
CARAVAN PARKS
Camber Sands Leisure Park Ltd.

New Lydd Road. Tel: (0797) 225555
Leisure Park Operators
Months Open: Easter to October 31st. Days Open: 7 days per
week. Hours Open: 24 Hours. All holidays except Christmas.
Superb clubhouse. Europa restaurant and bar. Entertainments
programme. Health club. Four indoor swimming pools.
Children's playground. Modern accommodation. Adjacent to
sandy beach. Close to the ancient port of Rye. Rates: From £80
per week to sleep 6 , inclusive of gas, electricity, and V.A.T.
Proprietor: Douglas Taylor.
Silver Sands Caravan Park
Lydd Road. Tel: (0797) 225282/225418

LEISURE CENTRE
Camber Putting Course
Old Lydd Road. Tel: (0797) 225485

THE WINDMILL AT CHAILEY

East Grinstead Road. Tel: (082 572) 2870

PUBLIC HOUSE
The Five Bells
Tel: (082 572) 2259

OTHER AMENITY
HOSPITAL
Chailey Heritage
St. George's, Haywards Heath Road. Tel: (082 572) 2112

CATSFIELD
North of Bexhill, on the road to Battle. The church
of St. Lawrence, not to be confused with the mag-
nificently spired Methodist church, contains a
memorial to Lady Annie Brassey, intrepid maritime explorer of the South Seas.
Population: 706.

PUBLIC HOUSE
White Hart Inn
The Green. Tel: (0424) 892650

OTHER AMENITIES
CARAVAN PARK
Tellis Coppice Caravan Park
A269. Tel: (042 46) 3969/4860

RIDING SCHOOL
Wilton House Riding Centre
The Bungalow, Broomham House. Tel: (0424) 892096

CHAILEY
Straddling the main road north of Lewes, between
the North Common and the South Common, with
the village proper in the middle. Justly most renowned for the Heritage Craft School, where children suffering from such debilitating diseases as
spina bifida and cerebral palsy are educated and
cared for.
Population: 2,313.

HOTEL
The King's Head Hotel

CHALVINGTON
A small peaceful village in the area north of the
South Downs before they disappear into the sea at
Eastbourne. There was a time when residents had
to pay a toll to their liege to cross the parish
boundary.
Population: 140.

PUBLIC HOUSE
Yew Tree Inn
Tel: (032 183) 326

CHIDDINGLY
This tiny village manages to retain an air of re-
moteness. The 130-foot spire of the church towers
over the village, and inside there is a monument to

St John Jefferays, Queen Elizabeth I's Chancellor, disfigured by locals who thought him related to Judge Jeffereys, the 'Hanging Judge'.
Population: 810.

PUBLIC HOUSE
The Six Bells Inn
Tel: (0825) 872227

🐾 🐾 🐾 🐾 🐾 🐾 🐾

COODEN
Now little more than the west suburb of Bexhill, it was once the site of a great wood stretching to the sea's edge. Indeed the stumps of trees are still visible at low tide.

HOTEL
Cooden Resort Hotel
Tel: (042 43) 2281
Traditional hotel on beach with adjacent golf course which gives our guests special rates. Direct line railway station to London and South East.
BEDROOMS: 16 Single, (16 en suite, 16 TV, 16 phone, 16 tea/coffee) B&B £ 56.50. 5 Double, (5 en suite, 5 TV, 5 phone, 5 tea/coffee) B&B £ 78.00. 10 Twin, (10 en suite, 10 TV, 10 phone, 10 tea/coffee) B&B £ 78.00. 6 Family, (6 en suite, 6 TV, 6 phone, 6 tea/coffee) RESTAURANT: Lunch: £ 11.50. Dinner: £ 15.50. House Wine: £8.00. HOTEL INFORMATION: CF. W. B. F. 60 space Car Park. Dogs. Sports Facilities: golf.
Weekend Breaks: 2 nights: £ 84.00. 3 nights: £ 126.00.
Allowance towards dinner: £ 15.00.

RESTAURANT
Dragon & Peacock Chinese Take Away
59 Cooden Sea Road. Tel: (042 43) 4036

CAFÉS & TEA ROOMS
Bungalow Cafe
Barnhorn Road. Tel: (042 43) 2258
Two Trees Cafe
37 Cooden Sea Road, Little Common. Tel: (042 43) 2066

OTHER AMENITIES
CARAVAN PARK
Sovereign View Association (Caravan Site)
Constable Farm, Barnhorn Road. Tel: (042 43) 5750

RIDING SCHOOL
The Whydown Riding Centre
Whydown Place, Whydown Road. Tel: (042 43) 6279

TAXI
Grey Taxis

Belinda , Riders Bolt. Tel: (042 43) 3888

🐾 🐾 🐾 🐾 🐾 🐾 🐾

COOKSBRIDGE
A village due north of Lewes, below the downs.

PUBLIC HOUSES
The Hopleaf
Tel: (0273) 400528
The Rainbow Inn
Tel: (0273) 400334

OTHER AMENITY
GARDEN CENTRE
Chubbs Garden Centre
Brickyard Nursery . Tel: (0273) 400218

🐾 🐾 🐾 🐾 🐾 🐾 🐾

COWBEECH
A tiny village in the wooded hilly countryside near Herstmonceux.

PUBLIC HOUSE
Merry Harriers
Tel: (0323) 833108

🐾 🐾 🐾 🐾 🐾 🐾 🐾

CRIPPS CORNER
In the wooded countryside north of Hastings, Cripps Corner is in fact a crossroads.

RESTAURANT
Olivers Restaurant
Tel: (058 083) 387

PUBLIC HOUSE
The White Hart
Tel: (058 083) 246

OTHER AMENITY
GARDEN CENTRE
Staplecross Shrub Centre
Brambles. Tel: (058 083) 678

🐾 🐾 🐾 🐾 🐾 🐾 🐾

CROSS IN HAND
Two miles west of Henfield, on an important road junction. There is an attractive post mill set on the central triangle.

PLACES OF INTEREST
Long Barn Motor Museum
Tel: (043 52) 3800

RESTAURANT
The Little Chef
Isenhurst Service Station. Tel: (043 52) 3187

🐾 🐾 🐾 🐾 🐾 🐾 🐾

CROWBOROUGH
With Maresfield and Forest Row, Crowborough is a corner of the triangle which marks out the Ashdown Forest. A relatively new town by Sussex standards, it is still growing. The current centre of the town is at Crowborough Cross.
Population: 17,485.

PLACES OF INTEREST
Cobblers Garden
A two acre garden designed by its owners for all season colour.
Days Open: Selected Sundays only. Hours Open: 2.30 - 5.30pm. Admission: £1.00. Children half price. Home made teas. No dogs. Plants for sale.

HOTEL
Winston Manor Hotel
Beacon Road. Tel: (0892) 652772
Comfortable 3 star hotel. 54 superb bedrooms with private facilities, health club, coffee shop. Dinner dances, conferences, meetings, weddings, functions.
BEDROOMS: 2 Single, (2 en suite, 2 TV, 2 phone, 2 tea/coffee) B&B £ 55.00 - £ 75.00. 52 Double, (52 en suite, 52 TV, 52 phone, 52 tea/coffee) B&B £ 75.00. RESTAURANT: English Cuisine. Lunch: £ 10.50. Tea: £ 6.00. Dinner: £ 14.50. House Wine: £ 7.00. À La Carte: £ 21.00. HOTEL INFORMATION: CF. W. B. F. 120 space Car Park. Sports Facilities: Golf nearby. Riding nearby. Credit Cards: Ac. Am. D. V. Recommendations: AA***. Weekend Breaks: 2 nights: £ 80.00.

GUEST HOUSE
Rocks House
Stone Cross. TN6 2SJ. Tel: (0892) 655612

RESTAURANTS
Akash Tandoori Restaurant
24 Crowborough Hill, Jarvis Brook. Tel: (0892) 661881/ 664647
Archers Restaurant
3 London Road. Tel: (0892) 654631
J. Bennett
1 St. Johns Road. Tel: (0892) 654526
Cosmo Barbecue Restaurant

6 The Broadway. Tel: (0892) 665296
Friendly 8 Restaurant
2 Sussex House, The Broadway. Tel: (0892) 665102/665143
Good Friend
Farningham Road. Tel: (0892) 662526
Pic-Ups
2 Brookfield Villas, Jarvis Brook, Crowborough Hill. Tel: (0892) 652570
The Pizza House
Belmont, 1a High Street. Tel: (0892) 654339
Rose of Bengal
3 Crowborough Hill. Tel: (0892) 653183/662252
Tsang's House
6 London Road. Tel: (0892) 653927
White Hart
Chapel Green. Tel: (0892) 52367
Winston Manor
Beacon Road. Tel: (0892) 652772

PUBLIC HOUSES
The Blue Anchor
Beacon Road. Tel: (0892) 654519
Boars Head Inn
Boars Head. Tel: (0892) 652412
The Bricklayers Arms
Whitehill Road. Tel: (0892) 654932
Coopers Arms
St. Johns. Tel: (0892) 654796
Crow & Gate
Poundgate. Tel: (0892) 661559
The Crowborough Cross
Beacon Road. Tel: (0892) 654009
The Half Moon
Friars Gate. Tel: (0892) 661270
The Plough & Horses
Walshes Road. Tel: (0892) 652614
Rose & Crown
White Hill. Tel: (0892) 654517

CAFÉ/TEA ROOMS
Pepperpot Coffee Bar
Unit 9, Fernbank Shopping Centre, High Street. Tel: (0892) 665295/665588

OTHER AMENITIES
CAR HIRE/SELF DRIVE
Croft Self Drive
Orchid Stables, Walshes Road. Tel: (0892) 662636/ 665121
D.B.S. Garages
Crowborough Hill, Jarvis Brook. Tel: (0892) 652175
Gilberts Garage
Warren Road. Tel: (0892) 652131/652132/661529
Stormont Vehicle Hire

Eridge Road. Tel: (0892) 665123

GARDEN CENTRES
The Garden Shop
Whitehill Road. Tel: (0892) 655766
Millbrook Garden Centre
Rotherfield Road, Jarvis Brook. Tel: (0892) 663822

HOSPITAL
Crowborough War Memorial Hospital
South View Road. Tel: (0892) 652284

LEISURE CENTRE
Goldsmiths Leisure Centre
Eridge Road. Tel: (0892) 665488

NIGHT CLUB
Valentines
The Broadway. Tel: (0892) 662168

RIDING SCHOOLS
T.H. Douglas
Pine Tree Farm, Fielden Road. Tel: (0892) 654195
The Equestrian Centre
Friars Gate Farm, Marden Hill. Tel: (0892) 661195

STORES
Woolworths plc
High Street. Tel: (0892) 653397

TAXIS
Arnold Cabs
126 Alderbrook Close. TN6 3DP Tel: (0892) 664339
Barry's Car Hire
16 Springfield Close. Tel: (0892) 654442
Crowborough Cab Company
2 Sussex View, Southview Road. Tel: (0892) 665522
Fairwestern Taxis
Croft Road Garage, Croft Road. Tel: (0892) 653113
Kandy Kars Tel: (0892) 667068

🐝 🐝 🐝 🐝 🐝 🐝 🐝

CROWHURST
Situated on a steep hillside on the road from Hastings to Battle. The church of St George has a 15th century tower with a Pelham buckle (see East Hoathly). Outside the church is a yew tree said to date back to King Harold's time, and beyond it are the ruins of a 13th century manor house.
Population: 802.

HOTEL
The Inn at Crowhurst

Station Road. Tel: (042 483) 488

PUBLIC HOUSE
Plough Inn
Hastings Road. Tel: (042 483) 310

OTHER AMENITIES
CARAVAN PARK
Brakes Coppice Farm Park
Forewood Lane. Tel: (0892) 322
Touring caravan and camping site
Months Open: Mar-Oct. Days Open: 7 days per week. Hours Open: Closes at dusk. Open on Bank Holidays. Small secluded site. Fishing lake. Drying room. Wooded walks. Toddlers play area. Rates: £4 per unit plus 50p per adult and 25p per child. Proprietors: Mr & Mrs R H Kemp.

GARDEN CENTRE
Glebe Farm Nurseries
Forewood Lane. Tel: (042 483) 285

🐝 🐝 🐝 🐝 🐝 🐝 🐝

DALLINGTON
A pleasantly remote village. The church spire is covered in stone slabs, rather than the usual shingle. It is also, unusually for Sussex, recessed, which may have led to 'Mad' Jack Fuller's ill-fated bet that he could see it from his lawn at Brightling Park, which resulted in his having the 'Sugar Loaf' built. (See Brightling.)
Population: 285.

RESTAURANT
Little Byres
Christmas Farm, Battle Road. Tel: (042 482) 230

🐝 🐝 🐝 🐝 🐝 🐝 🐝

DENTON
Just outside Newhaven and barely distinguishable from South Heighton.

PUBLIC HOUSE
The Flying Fish
42, Denton Road. Tel: (0273) 515440

🐝 🐝 🐝 🐝 🐝 🐝 🐝

DITCHLING
An attractive village of Tudor and Georgian houses built around a crossroads, north of the downs. 'Diccelingas' was once the administrative centre of a vast Royal Estate. It now has a reputation for its

ANNE OF CLEVES HOUSE DITCHLING

good quality arts and crafts. There is some dispute whether Anne of Cleves House had anything to do with England's first divorcee.

Population: 1,768.

PLACES OF INTEREST

Ditchling Beacon
The remains of a hill fort on the South Downs Way. Wonderful views across the Weald.

Ditchling Museum
Tel: (0273) 4744

History In Brass
Lower Rookery, 46 Lewes Road.
Tel: (0273) 2153

RESTAURANT

Raphael's Restaurant
2, South Street. Tel: (079 18) 2704

PUBLIC HOUSES

The Bull Hotel
2, High Street. Tel: (0273) 3147

The North Star
19, North End . Tel: (0273) 3970

The White Horse Inn
61, West Street. Tel: (0273) 2006

OTHER AMENITIES

ART GALLERIES

Chichester House Gallery
High Street. Tel: (0273) 4167
Art Gallery
Months Open: All. Days Open: Every day Sun Mon & Wed by appointment only. Hours Open: 11am-1pm/2.30pm-5pm. Not open on Bank Holidays. Paintings, books, greetings cards, gifts etc. Proprietors: Mr & Mrs J Hunter.

The Craftsman Gallery
8, High Street. Tel: (0273) 5246

TAXI

Gerry's Taxis
17, Neville Cottage. Tel: (0273) 3332

🐝 🐝 🐝 🐝 🐝 🐝 🐝

DITCHLING COMMON

PUBLIC HOUSE

The Royal Oak Inn
Jacobs Post. Tel: (044 484) 263

🐝 🐝 🐝 🐝 🐝 🐝 🐝

DUDDLESWELL

Situated between Maresfield and Hartfield, the village bestrides the Roman road which ran from

Lewes to London. This may explain how this hamlet, so far from the coast, claims once to have been the haunt of smugglers.

CAFÉ/TEA ROOMS
Duddleswell Tea Rooms
Tel: (082 571) 2126

OTHER AMENITIES
GARDEN CENTRE
Ashdown Forest Gardens
Tel: (082 571) 2300/3118

🐾 🐾 🐾 🐾 🐾 🐾 🐾

EAST DEAN
At the bottom of a steep hill on the A 259 west of Eastbourne. A downland village of flint walls, grouped around a rectangular green. To the south, the road goes on a scenic meander, eventually coming to the spectacular view of Beachy Head.
Population: 1,007.

The
BIRLING GAP HOTEL
EAST DEAN, EASTBOURNE

HOTEL
Birling Gap Hotel
Seven Sisters. Tel: (0323) 423197/423163
Magnificent 'Seven Sisters' clifftop setting. Bedrooms fully en suite. Country views, sea and beach. Olde Worlde thatched bar, restaurant and coffee shop.
BEDROOMS: 1 Single, (1 en suite, 1 TV, 1 phone, 1 tea/coffee) £28.75. 6 Double (6 en suite, 6 TV, 6 phone, 6 tea/coffee)£20.00 pp. 2 Twin, (2 en suite, 2 TV, 2 phone, 2 tea/coffee) £20.00 pp 3 Family (3 en suite, 3 TV, 3 phone, 3 tea/coffee) £20.00 pp. RESTAURANT: Traditional Cuisine. Lunch: £ 5.25. Tea: £ 1.25. Dinner: £ 6.50. Hse Wine: £ 4.95. À La Carte: £ 6.50. Specialities: Locally caught fish. HOTEL INFORMATION: CF. W. B. F. 100 space car park. Dogs. Sports Facilities: Local golf & riding. Fishing. Credit Cards: Ac. Am. D. V.

RESTAURANT
Grimaldi Restaurant
The Green. Tel: (03215) 2384

PUBLIC HOUSE
The Tiger Inn
The Green. Tel: (032 15) 3209

EAST HOATHLY
A compact village straddling the A 22, on a bad 90° bend. The church, though largely rebuilt, has one of the Pelham towers (the others are at Chiddingly, Laughton and Ripe), a squat 15th century structure built by the Pelham family, with their motif, a belt buckle, carved either side of the door.
Population: 830.

PUBLIC HOUSES
The Foresters Arms
South Street. Tel: (082 584) 208
Kings Head
Tel: (082 584) 238

OTHER AMENITY
CARAVAN PARK
Caravan Club Ltd.
Broomfield Farm. Tel: (0825) 872242

🐾 🐾 🐾 🐾 🐾 🐾 🐾

EASTBOURNE
Sandwiched between two Martello Towers, Eastbourne's three miles of elegant sea-front, devoid of any shops, has grand hotels, white Georgian parades, a fine Victorian pier and wide promenade, and is rivalled only by Brighton as the finest classical sea-front in England. Eastbourne offers just about every facility any holiday-maker could wish; swimming, wind-surfing, sailing and fishing. A prosperous town, it exudes solid respectability and genteel relaxation. Meaning 'East stream', the old town is to the west, just off the Brighton road, grouped around the old parish church dedicated to St Mary. Like nearly all the resorts on the south coast, Eastbourne was created after 1850, in this case by the Duke of Devonshire who laid out the Estate, and is immortalised in statue form, and by the numerous edifices bearing his name. Eastbourne, like Brighton, also has a thriving conference business. It also hosts a prestigeous Womens Lawn Tennis competition immediately prior to Wimbledon.
Population: 77,963.

PLACES OF INTEREST
Beachy Head
Reaching 575 feet above the sea, this is the tallest headland on the south coast and a magnificent spectacle. The old light-house, now converted, was used in the filming of the BBC series 'Life and Loves of a She Devil'.
How We Lived Then Museum
20, Cornfield Terrace. Tel: (0323) 37143

BEACHY HEAD, THE TALLEST HEADLAND ON THE SOUTH COAST

Redoubt Fortress

Tel: (0323) 410300

Built 1805-10. A circular ten-gun fortress with casemates for a garrison of 350 men. Contains the Regimental Museum of the Royal Sussex Regiment and the Queen's Royal Irish Hussars.

43

Months Open: Easter - October. Days Open: Everyday. Hours Open: 10am - 5.30pm. Collections of cannons on the battlement.

Royal National Lifeboat Institution Museum

Grand Parade.

Tel: (0323) 30717

Many lifeboats from the earliest date till the present time and the various equipment used in the lifeboat service.

Months Open: March - January 1. Days Open: Everyday. Hours Open: 9.30am- 5.30pm.

Towner Art Gallery & Local History Museum

Manor Gardens, High Street, Old Town.

Tel: (0323) 411688

Large permanent collection of 19th and 20th century British Art. Combined with local history from prehistoric to the Edwardian era, set in an 18th century manor house in public gardens.

Months Open: All year. Days Open: Everyday (except Mondays from November - March). Hours Open: Mon - Sat 10am - 5pm; Sun 2 - 5pm. Admission: Free.

Wish Tower Invasion Museum

King Edward Parade.

Tel: (0323) 410440

One of the series of Martello towers built between 1805 and 1810 as part of the defences against an invasion by Napoleon. The exhibitions illustrate the historical background, armament and manning of these forts. Displays include weapons, uniforms and models.

Months Open: Easter - October. Days Open: Everyday. Hours Open: 10am - 5.30pm.

HOTELS

Adrian House Private Hotel

24, Selwyn Road. BN21 2LR. Tel: (0323) 20372

Afton Hotel

2 - 6 , Cavendish Place. Tel: (0323) 33162

Albermarle Hotel

Marine Parade. Tel: (0323) 30666

Alexandra Hotel

Grand Parade. Tel: (0323) 20131

Alfriston Hotel

16, Lushington Road. Tel: (0323) 20400

Ambleside Hotel

24, Elms Avenue. Tel: (0323) 24991

Arden Hotel

17, Burlington Place. Tel: (0323) 639639

A Victorian family-run hotel. Close to sea, town, theatres & conference facilities. Caters for non-smokers only.

BEDROOMS: 2 Single, (2 en suite, 2 tea/coffee) B&B £ 16.00 - £18.00. 3 Double, (3 en suite, 3 tea/coffee) B&B £ 16.00 - £ 18.00. 4 Twin, (3 en suite, 4 tea/coffee) B&B £ 16.00 - £ 20.00. 1 Family, (1 en suite, 1 tea/coffee) £ 16.00–£ 18.00 Credit Cards: Ac.

Arundel Hotel

43, Carlisle Road. Tel: (0323) 639481

Avalon Court Hotel

49, Pevensey Road. Tel: (0323) 24243

BEDROOMS: 5 Single, (5 TV, 5 tea/coffee) B&B £ 12.00 - £15.00. 6 Double, (6 TV, 6 tea/coffee) 7 Twin, (7 TV, 7 tea/coffee) 4 Family, (4 TV, 4 tea/coffee).

Weekend Breaks: 2 nights: £ 25.00. 3 nights: £ 35.00. Allowance towards dinner: £ 3.10.

Avalon Hotel

39/41, Cavendish Place. Tel: (0323) 26993

Situated opposite coach station

BEDROOMS: 4 Single, (4 TV, 4 tea/coffee) 6 Double, (6 TV, 6 tea/coffee) 6 Twin, (6 TV, 6 tea/coffee) 2 Family, (2 TV, 2 tea/coffee)

Weekend Breaks: 2 nights: £ 25.00. 3 nights: £ 35.00. Allowance towards dinner: £ 3.00.

Avondale Hotel

77/79 , Royal Parade. Tel: (0323) 23510

The Balmoral Private Hotel

7, Silverdale Road. Tel: (0323) 34901

The Bay Lodge Hotel

61/62 , Royal Parade. Tel: (0323) 32515

The Beach Haven

61, Pevensey Road. Tel: (0323) 26195

Beechwood Hotel

Hartfield Road. Tel: (0323) 23020

Belsaye Hotel

Ratton Road. Tel: (0323) 20287

The Beverley Hotel

14, Burlington Place. Tel: (0323) 642749

Bisenden Private Hotel

91, Pevensey Road. Tel: (0323) 26467

Bourne House Hotel

16, Bourne Street. Tel: (0323) 21981

Boyne House

10 - 12, St Aubyns Road. Tel: (0323) 28494

Brookside Hotel

19/21, Pevensey Road. Tel: (0323) 24408

Brownings Hotel

28, Upperton Road. Tel: (0323) 24358

The Burlington Hotel

Grand Parade. Tel: (0323) 22724

The Camberley Hotel

27/29, Elms Avenue. Tel: (0323) 23789

Carlton Court Hotel

10, Wilmington Square. Tel: (0323) 32787

The Cavendish Hotel

30, Burlington Place. Tel: (0323) 22127

Chalk Farm House Hotel

Coopers Hill. Tel: (0323) 503800

The Cherry Tree Hotel

15, Silverdale Road. Tel: (0323) 22406

Colincourt Private Hotel

19, Hyde Gardens. Tel: (0323) 23402

Congress Hotel

31/41, Carlisle Road. Tel: (0323) 32118

EASTBOURNE SEA-FRONT

Cornfield Hotel
15, Cornfield Terrace. Tel: (0323) 28176
Courtlands Hotel
68, Royal Parade. BN22 7AQ. Tel: (0323) 21068
The Croft Hotel
18, Prideaux Road. Tel: (0323) 22390
The Cromwell Hotel
23, Cavendish Place. Tel: (0323) 25288
The Cumberland Hotel
Grand Parade. Tel: (0323) 30342
Davington Private Hotel
6, Silverdale Road. Tel: (0323) 23165
Denstone House Hotel
9, College Road, Devonshire Park. BN21 4JA.
Tel: (0323) 411000
Devonia House
74, Royal Parade. Tel: (0323) 20059
Diplocks Hotel
Terminus Road. Tel: (0323) 25141
Downland Hotel & Restaurant
37, Lewes Road. BN21 2BU. Tel: (0323) 32689
Edelweiss Hotel
10 / 12, Elms Avenue. Tel: (0323) 32071
Ellesmere Hotel

11, Wilmington Square. Tel: (0323) 31463
The Elm Park Hotel
20, Cavendish Place. Tel: (0323) 411511
The Elm-Hyrst Hotel
37, Elms Avenue. Tel: (0323) 411444
The Elms Hotel
19 / 21, Elms Avenue. Tel: (0323) 23765
Eventons Hotel
72, Royal Parade. Tel: (0323) 30745
Excelsior Hotel
Cavendish Place. Tel: (0323) 22218
Fairdene Private Hotel
3, Marine Parade. Tel: (0323) 30926
Fairlands Private Hotel
15, Lascelles Terrace. Tel: (0323) 33287
Fairlight Hotel
41, Silverdale Road. Tel: (0323) 21770
Falcondale House Private Hotel
5, Southcliff Avenue. Tel: (0323) 643633
Farrar's Hotel
3 / 5, Wilmington Gardens. Tel: (0323) 23737
Flamingo Private Hotel
20, Enys Road. BN21 2DN. Tel: (0323) 21654
BEDROOMS: 2 Single, (2 en suite, 2 TV, 2 tea/coffee) B&B

45

£ 17.50 - £ 20.00. 5 Double, (5 en suite, 5 TV, 5 tea/coffee) B&B
£ 17.505 Twin, (5 en suite, 5 TV, 5 tea/coffee) B&B £ 17.50.

The Four Seasons Hotel
11 / 12, Royal Parade. Tel: (0323) 22146

The Gladwyn Hotel
16, Blackwater Road. Tel: (0323) 33142

Glamis Guest House
15, Elms Avenue. Tel: (0323) 32907
BEDROOMS: B&B £ 12.00 - £ 15.00. 6 Double, (2 en suite, 6 tea/coffee) B&B £ 15.00 - £ 18.00.

Glastonbury Hotel
4 / 9, Royal Parade. BN22 7AR. Tel: (0323) 24253
BEDROOMS: 19 Single, (4 en suite, 19 tea/coffee) B&B £ 14.00 - £ 21.00. 13 Double, (7 en suite, 13 tea/coffee) B&B £ 13.00 - £ 21.00. 52 Twin, (37 en suite, 52 tea/coffee) B&B £ 12.00 - £ 22.00. 2 Family, (1 en suite, 2 tea/coffee) £ 14.00–£ 22.00 RESTAURANT: Family service Cuisine. Lunch: £ 3.50. Dinner: £ 5.00. House Wine: £ 6.00. Credit Cards: Ac.
Weekend Breaks: 2 nights: £ 24.00. 3 nights: £ 36.00. Allowance towards dinner: £ 3.50.

Gleneagles Hotel
54, Royal Parade. Tel: (0323) 25492

Glenroy Hotel
10, Royal Parade. Tel: (0323) 30486

The Grand Hotel
King Edwards Parade. Tel: (0323) 412345

Granville Hotel
21, Cavendish Place. Tel: (0323) 25304

Grays Private Hotel
Elms Avenue. Tel: (0323) 23539

The Greenwich Hotel
South Street. Tel: (0323) 639761

Haddon Hall Hotel
Devonshire Place. Tel: (0323) 640953

The Halcyon Hotel
8, South Cliff. Tel: (0323) 23710

Hanburies Hotel
4, Hardwick Road. Tel: (0323) 30698

Heatherdene Private Hotel
26/28, Elms Avenue. Tel: (0323) 23598

Heatherleigh Hotel
66, Royal Parade. Tel: (0323) 21167

The Hilton Hotel
35/38, Royal Parade. Tel: (0323) 23174

Holiday Hotels
19, Jevington Gardens. Tel: (0323) 25010

Hydro Hotel
South Cliff. Tel: (0323) 20643

The Imperial Hotel
Devonshire Place. Tel: (0323) 411043

Ingham House Hotel
10 / 12, Carlisle Road. Tel: (0323) 34009

Iverna Hotel
32, Marine Parade. Tel: (0323) 30768

Ivydene Family Hotel
5 / 6, Hampden Terrace. Tel: (0323) 20547

James Hotel
51, Jevington Gardens. Tel: (0323) 32503

The Jevington Hotel
9 - 11, Jevington Gardens. Tel: (0323) 32093

Langham Hotel
Royal Parade. Tel: (0323) 31451

Lansdowne Hotel
King Edwards Parade. BN21 4EE. Tel: (0323) 25174

Lantern Lodge Hotel
57, Cavendish Place. Tel: (0323) 639096

Lathom Hotel
6, Howard Square. Tel: (0323) 641986

Le Chalet Hotel
7, Marine Parade. Tel: (0323) 20029

Little Crookham Private Hotel
16, South Cliff Avenue. Tel: (0323) 34160

Lynwood Hotel
33, Jevington Gardens. Tel: (0323) 638716

Majestic Hotel
26, Royal Parade. Tel: (0323) 30311

Malvern House Private Hotel
82, Royal Parade. BN22 7AE. Tel: (0323) 21969

Mansion Hotel
Grand Parade. Tel: (0323) 27411

Marina Hotel
86, Royal Parade. Tel: (0323) 20297

Marine Hotel
61, Seaside. Tel: (0323) 20464

Mascot Hotel
60, Pevensey Road. Tel: (0323) 21839

Medwyn Court Private Hotel
27, Carlisle Road. Tel: (0323) 28144

Melody Hotel
65, Pevensey Road. Tel: (0323) 26923

Merryfield Hotel
51, Royal Parade. Tel: (0323) 23696

Merton Hotel
49, Jevington Gardens. Tel: (0323) 21943

Merville Private Hotel
41, Ceylon Place. BN22 8AA. Tel: (0323) 27437

Mowbray Hotel
2, Lascelles Terrace. Tel: (0323) 20012

New Alwyn Hotel
15-17, Jevington Gardens. Tel: (0323) 24169

New Elizabethan Hotel
4, St Annes Road. Tel: (0323) 24169

The New Elmcroft Hotel
53, Jevington Gardens. Tel: (0323) 21263

New Garden Pool Hotel
13/15, Devonshire Place. Tel: (0323) 24005

New Wilmington Hotel
25, Compton Street. Tel: (0323) 21219

THE GARDENS ON EASTBOURNE SEA-FRONT

New Windsor Hotel
9, Silverdale Road. Tel: (0323) 30707
Nirvana
32, Redoubt Road. Tel: (0323) 22603
Oakwood Hotel
28, Jevington Gardens. Tel: (0323) 21900
Orchard House Private Hotel
10, Old Orchard Road. Tel: (0323) 23682
Park View Hotel
8, Wilmington Gardens. Tel: (0323) 21242
Paron Hotel
72-76, Pevensey Road. Tel: (0323) 23374
Peregrine House Hotel
53, Cavendish Place. Tel: (0323) 36315
Perran Hotel
7 / 9, Bourne Street. Tel: (0323) 23384
Princes Hotel
Lascelles Terrace. Tel: (0323) 22056
Queens Cliff Hotel
24, Carew Road. Tel: (0323) 26723
The Queens Hotel
Marine Parade. Tel: (0323) 22822

The Ranworth Christian Hotel
86/88, Pevensey Road. Tel: (0323) 33520
The hotel is near the seafront, shops and theatres and offers
a homely atmosphere.
BEDROOMS: 5 single B&B £ 10.00 - £11.00. 1 Double, (1 tea/
coffee) B&B £ 10.00 - £11.00. 3 Twin, (3 tea/coffee) B&B £10.00
- £ 11.00. 5 Family, (5 tea/coffee) £ 10.00–£ 11.00
Weekend Breaks: 2 nights: £ 32.00. 3 nights: £ 42.00.
The Red Lion
99, Wish Hill. Tel: (0323) 502062
Regent Hotel
3, Cavendish Place. Tel: (0323) 31258
Revelstoke Hotel
11, Lascelles Terrace. Tel: (0323) 25186
Reymar Hotel
4, Cambridge Road. Tel: (0323) 24649
Reynolds Court Hotel Ltd
1 - 13, Cambridge Road. Tel: (0323) 24709
Richmond House Hotel
3, Elms Avenue. Tel: (0323) 32779
The Ridings Hotel
84/85, Royal Parade. Tel: (0323) 21896
Riftswood Guest House

14, Cambridge Road. Tel: (0323) 26982

Rowsley Private Hotel

14/16, Elms Avenue. Tel: (0323) 32584

BEDROOMS: 3 Single, (3 TV, 3 tea/coffee) B&B £ 12.65 - £ 14.95. 6 Double, (1 en suite, 6 TV, 6 tea/coffee) B&B £ 12.65 - £ 14.95. 2 Twin, (2 TV, 2 tea/coffee) B&B £ 12.65 - £ 14.95. 2 Family, (2 en suite, 2 TV, 2 tea/coffee) £ 12.65–£ 14.95

Weekend Breaks: 2 nights: £ 25.30. 3 nights: £ 37.95. Allowance towards dinner: £ 3.50.

The Royal Hotel

8 / 9, Marine Parade. Tel: (0323) 24027

Saffrons Hotel

30, Jevington Gardens. Tel: (0323) 25539

San Remo Private Hotel

29, Royal Parade. Tel: (0323) 21831

Sandhurst Hotel

Grand Parade. Tel: (0323) 27868

BEDROOMS: 25 Single, (13 en suite, 25 TV, 25 phone, 25 tea/coffee) 10 Double, (10 en suite, 10 TV, 10 phone, 10 tea/coffee) 23 Twin, (23 en suite, 23 TV, 23 phone, 23 tea/coffee) 2 Family, (2 en suite, 2 TV, 2 phone, 2 tea/coffee) RESTAURANT: Traditional Cuisine. Lunch: £ 7.50. Dinner: £ 10.50. House Wine: £ 7.30. Specialities: Carvery. HOTEL INFORMATION: CF . W. B. F. Credit Cards: Ac. Am. D. V.

Weekend Breaks: 2 nights: £ 46.00.

The Savoy Court Hotel

11, Cavendish Place. Tel: (0323) 23132

Saxon Hotel

43/47, Ceylon Place. Tel: (0323) 21521

Sea Beach House Hotel

39-40, Marine Parade. Tel: (0323) 410458

Seaford Private Hotel

Silverdale Road. Tel: (0323) 20367

The Sheldon Hotel

11, Burlington Place. Tel: (0323) 24120

Sherwood Hotel

7, Lascelles Terrace. Tel: (0323) 24002

Silverwood Hotel

29, Carlisle Road. Tel: (0323) 20438

Southcroft Private Hotel

15, South Cliff Avenue. Tel: (0323) 29071

Southdown Hotel

Howard Square. Tel: (0323) 30129

St Briac Hotel

81, Royal Parade. Tel: (0323) 28939

St Helens Hotel

Marine Parade. Tel: (0323) 30005

St Omer Private Hotel

Royal Parade. Tel: (0323) 22152

Stanley House Hotel

9/10 Howard Square. BN21 4BQ. Tel: (0323) 31393

Situated in Eastbourne's premier square, recently totally refurbished. Very convenient for Conference Centre, theatre, seafront and shops. Open all year.

STANLEY HOUSE HOTEL, EASTBOURNE

BEDROOMS: 3 Single, (3 en suite, 3 tea/coffee) B&B £ 15.00 - £ 20.00. 6 Double, (6 en suite, 6 tea/coffee) B&B £ 30.00 - £ 40.00. 11 Twin, (11 en suite, 11 tea/coffee) B&B £ 30.00 - £ 40.00. 6 Family, (6 en suite, 6 tea/coffee) £ 30.00–£ 40.00. RESTAURANT: Traditional Cuisine. Lunch: £ 5.00. Tea: £ 3.00. Dinner: £ 10.00. House Wine: £ 5.95. À La Carte: £ 7.50. HOTEL INFORMATION: CF. W. B. F.

Stirling House Hotel

5 / 7, Cavendish Place. BN21 3EJ. Tel: (0323) 32263

Stratford Private Hotel

59, Cavendish Place. Tel: (0323) 24051

Sussex Hotel

Cornfield Terrace. Tel: (0323) 27681

Swanland Hotel

29, Marine Parade. Tel: (0323) 645098

Swanley Court Hotel

18, Trinity Trees. Tel: (0323) 29298

Tiverton House Hotel

13, Hartington Place. Tel: (0323) 24784

Tor View Hotel

27, Jevington Gardens. Tel: (0323) 20466

Ventura Hotel

48, Pevensey Road. Tel: (0323) 22939

Vernon House Hotel

1, Compton Street. Tel: (0323) 20803

The Victoria Hotel

Latimer Road. Tel: (0323) 22673

Vienna Private Hotel

15, Bourne Street. Tel: (0323) 20345

Waverley Hotel

42, Ashford Road. Tel: (0323) 642606

Weyanoke Hotel

23, Royal parade. Tel: (0323) 31398

Wish Tower Hotel

King Edwards Parade. Tel: (0323) 22676

Worcester House Hotel

77, Pevensey Road. Tel: (0323) 21601

Wynstay Private Hotel

13, Lewes Road. Tel: (0323) 21550

Ye Goode Intente Hotel
11, Cornfield Terrace. Tel: (0323) 23688
York House Hotel
14-22, Royal Parade. Tel: (0323) 412918

GUEST HOUSES

Alandale Guest House
25, Cavendish Place. Tel: (0323) 24638
Aliston Guest House
45, Cavendish Place. Tel: (0323) 27202
All Seasons Guest House
27, Cavendish Place. Tel: (0323) 23156
Ambria & Connaught
87, Pevensey Road. Tel: (0323) 36632
Andorra Guest House
86, Longstone Road. Tel: (0323) 29447
Annabelle Private Hotel
35, Elms Avenue. Tel: (0323) 21102
Anneford Guest House
33, Pevensey Road. Tel: (0323) 462103
Appledor
35, Ceylon Place. Tel: (0323) 21299
Ashfield House
104, Pevensey Road. Tel: (0323) 638520
Avalon Guest House
64 - 66, Pevensey Road. Tel: (0323) 22695
Avon Guest House
40, Lushington Road. Tel: (0323) 34961
Barnard House
99, Pevensey Road. Tel: (0323) 25592
Bayview Guest House
55, Royal Parade. Tel: (0323) 24964
Beach House Hotel
11, Marine Parade. Tel: (0323) 411864
Beachy Rise
20, Beachy Head Road. Tel: (0323) 639171
Bella Vista
30, Redoubt Road. Tel: (0323) 24222
Belmead Guest house
52, Ceylon Place. Tel: (0323) 21101
Belville Guest House
25, Bourne Street. Tel: (0323) 33689
Benvar Guest House
68, Seaside. Tel: (0323) 25675
Blairgowrie Guest House
108, Pevensey Road. Tel: (0323) 695542/26796
Blechingly Guest House
102, Pevensey Road . Tel: (0323) 27953
Bourne - Lea Guest House
93, Langney Road. Tel: (0323) 20648
Bracken Guest House
3 Hamden Terrace, Latimer Road. Tel: (0323) 25779
Burnbrae Guest House
44, Cavendish Place. Tel: (0323) 21561

Burne Holme Guest House
54, Ceylon Place. Tel: (0323) 24823
R. A. Cable
37, Cavendish Place. Tel: (0323) 21897
Cambridge House Guest House
6, Cambridge Road. Tel: (0323) 21100
Carinya Guest House
37, Pevensey Road. Tel: (0323) 31745
Chalfont Guest House
27, Ceylon Place. Tel: (0323) 23866
Charming guest house close to sea, shops ans theatres. Offers peaceful accommodation and tranquility. Vegetarians welcome. Pay phone.
Months Open: 12. Number of Bedrooms: 5. B&B per person: £12 per night. TV in rooms. Pets welcome. Evening meals. Proprietor: James Miller.
L.W. Champion
63, Pevensey Road. Tel: (0323) 23928
Chaos
16, Lewes Road. Tel: (0323) 22343
S. Clarke
6, St. Aubyns Road. Tel: (0323) 28266
Clovelly Guest House
10, Bourne Street. Tel: (0323) 20093
Coatham Guest House
114, Pevensey Road. Tel: (0323) 25979
Costi Anna Bella Vista Guest House
Elm Avenue. Tel: (0323) 28265
Courtney Guest House
97, Langney Road. Tel: (0323) 655940
Courtney House
53, Royal Parade. Tel: (0323) 32697
Cranleigh Guest House
29, Ceylon Place. Tel: (0323) 23745
Cuckmere House
20, South Cliff Avenue. Tel: (0323) 20492
Situated in a peaceful tree-lined avenue close to the theatres, winter garden and one minute from the sea. Excellent food and a comfortable home atmosphere. Licenced.
Months Open: 12. Number of Bedrooms: 6. (6 with bathroom). B&B per person: £15 per night. TV in rooms. Evening meals. Proprietor: Ivan Dent.
Dalbury Guest House
26, Bourne Street. Tel: (0323) 21514
Davena
92, Royal Parade. Tel: (0323) 27623
Delladale Lodge Guest House
35, Lewes Road. Tel: (0323) 22799
Delmar Guest House
8, Cambridge Road. Tel: (0323) 34823
Desmonds Guest House
40, Cavendish Place. Tel: (0323) 26684
Dovercourt Guest House
95, Langney Road. Tel: (0323) 38211

East Dean Guest House
18, St. Aubyns Road. Tel: (0323) 22204
Edelweiss Hotel
10 - 12, Elms Avenue. Tel: (0323) 32071/33963
The Edwardian
9, Southcliff Avenue. Tel: (0323) 640660
M. Emmet
122/123, Royal Parade. Tel: (0323) 30791
Far End Guest House
139, Royal Parade. Tel: (0323) 25666
Fenstanton Guest House
22, Ceylon Place. Tel: (0323) 26790
Florence Guest House
31, Elms Avenue. Tel: (0323) 26095
Gainsboro' Christian Guest House
19, Burlington Place. Tel: (0323) 410919
Christian Guest House with fellowship morning and evening. Near sea-front churches. For all denominations. Chair lift from 1st to 2nd floor, and ground to lower-ground
Months Open: November - September. Number of Bedrooms: 23. B&B per person: £12. Evening meals. 7 space car park. Proprietors: Arthur & Lily Briffitt
Garfield
90, Royal Parade. Tel: (0323) 410919
Gilday Hotel
1, Marine Parade. Tel: (0323) 21818
Glen Park Guest House
42, Cavendish Place. Tel: (0323) 34413
Glyndare
62, Pevensey Road. Tel: (0323) 34376
Grove Lodge Guest House
25, Pevensey Road. Tel: (0323) 31315
Hadyn House
44, Langney Road. Tel: (0323) 21740
Hazleden Guest House
43, Cavendish Place. Tel: (0323) 23933
Heathercroft Guest House
2 Hampden Terrace, Latimer Road. Tel: (0323) 25134
Huckleberry Guest House
7, Southcliff Avenue. Tel: (0323) 21679
Iandron Guest House
24, Borne Street. Tel: (0323) 23006
Idena Guest House
64, Ceylon Place. Tel: (0323) 26848
Jersey Lodge Hotel
39, Ceylon Place. Tel: (0323) 28857
Karoy Guest House
15, Rylstone Road . Tel: (0323) 39583
N.Z. Karsa
1, Elm Road. Tel: (0323) 21122
Kenway Guest House
56, Royal Parade. Tel: (0323) 29895
Kildare Guest House

27, Pevensey Road. Tel: (0323) 28240
Kings Lynn Guest House
95, Pevensey Road. Tel: (0323) 22359
Kingsmere Guest House
14, St. Aubyns Road. Tel: (0323) 21889
Kingston House
4, St. Aubyns Road. Tel: (0323) 640841
Knelworth Guest House
116, Pevensey Road. Tel: (0323) 28734
Koala Guest House
12, Bourne Street. Tel: (0323) 28334
The Langham
16, Charlotte Street. Tel: (0323) 682843
Lascelles Private Hotel
3, Lascelles Terrace. Tel: (0323) 20633
Lena Guest House
52/54, Ashford Road. Tel: (0323) 24706
E.E. Lewis
62, Ceylon Place. Tel: (0323) 29211
The Links Guest House
72, Meads Road. Tel: (0323) 30319
Linton Guest House
71, Langney Road. Tel: (0323) 28769
Loriston Guest House
17, St Aubyns Road. Tel: (0323) 26193
Madelaine Guest House
36, Redoubt Road. Tel: (0323) 23287
Mayvere
12, Cambridge Road. Tel: (0323) 29580
Melbourne
106, Pevensey Road. Tel: (0323) 34874
Merrywood Guest House
15, Cambridge Road. Tel: (0323) 25116
Minerva Guest Home
26a, Bourne Street. Tel: (0323) 34103
Months Open: 12. Number of Bedrooms: 6. B&B per person: £12.50. TV in rooms. Off-street parking.
Modena Guest House
68, Ceylon Place. Tel: (0323) 36307
Mona Lisa Guest House
15, St. Aubyns Road. Tel: (0323) 30000
Monckton Villa
35, Rylstone Road. Tel: (0323) 25732
Monsadale Guest House
44, Ashford Road. Tel: (0323) 30746
T. Norman
75, Pevensey Road. Tel: (0323) 31389
Osborne Guest House
77, Langley Road. Tel: (0323) 22276
Oxford House
35, Cavendish Place. Tel: (0323) 24860
Pendennif
51, Ceylon Place. Tel: (0323) 24595
Penrith Guest House

20, St. Aubyns Road. Tel: (0323) 21709

Pevensey Lodge

27, Pevensey Road. Tel: (0323) 649539

Richmond Guest House

3, Elms Avenue. Tel: (0323) 685230

Riviera Guest House

72, Langney Road. Tel: (0323) 33561

Rockville Hotel

20/22 , Bourne Street. BN21 3ER. Tel: (0323) 38488

Small family run hotel with TV lounge and bar. Good home cooking, friendly atmosphere, close to all amenities. *Months Open: All year. Number of Bedrooms: 13. (3 with bathroom). B&B per person: £12. Pets welcome. Dinner optional. Proprietors: Ann and Eric Murchie.*

Rosedale Guest House

13, Bourne Street. Tel: (0323) 20215

Sainvia Private Hotel

19, Ceylon Place. Tel: (0323) 25943

Sea Breeze Guest House

6, Marine Road. Tel: (0323) 25440

Seacroft

9, St. Aubyns Road . Tel: (0323) 35433

Shawley House

38, Cavendish Place. Tel: (0323) 27451

Shebern Guest House

15, St. Aubyns. Tel: (0323) 30000

Southview Hotel

38, Royal Parade. Tel: (0323) 20322

Sovereign View Guest House

93, Royal Parade. Tel: (0323) 21657

St. Claire Guest House

70, Pevensey Road. Tel: (0323) 29483

St. Malo Guest House

1, St. Aubyns Road. Tel: (0323) 34871

Stanford House

78, Pevensey Road. Tel: (0323) 33395

Stirling House

5, Cavendish Place. Tel: (0323) 28849

Stranraer Guest House

43, Pevensey Road. Tel: (0323) 27647

Sullom Voe Guest House

110, Pevensey Road. Tel: (0323) 24715

Sutherland House

4, Marine Road. Tel: (0323) 33221

Trenault Guest Hotel

5, St. Aubyns Road . Tel: (0323) 24161

Tudor House

5, Marine Road. Tel: (0323) 21796

Upperton House Hotel

Upperton Gardens. Tel: (0323) 20309

Venice House

50, Langley Road. Tel: (0323) 25061

Ventnor House

Langley Road. Tel: (0323) 37873

Willowfield House

6, Willowfield Road . Tel: (0323) 31957

RESTAURANTS

Acropolis Restaurant and Taverna

209, Terminus Road. Tel: (0323) 22708

American Beefyland Restaurant

43, Seaside Road. Tel: (0323) 37798

Ashoka Tandoori Restaurant

28, Cornfield Road. Tel: (0323) 20347

Athens Restaurant

195, Terminus Road. Tel: (0323) 33278

Bannisters Wine Bar

6 Church Street, Old Town. Tel: (0323) 39710

The Beachy Head Pub

Beachy Head. BN20 7YA Tel: (0323) 28060

Beefeaters Restaurant

215, Terminus Road. Tel: (0323) 643352

Bistro Byron

6, Crown Street. Tel: (0323) 20171

Blue Moon

100, Seaside. Tel: (0323) 27473

Bogeys Restaurant

11, Carlisle Road. Tel: (0323) 644029

Bonne Bouche

10, North Street. Tel: (0323) 38836

Brown's Restaurant

17, Carlisle Road. Tel: (0323) 28837

The Capricorn

89, Seaside. Tel: (0323) 639331

Casa Pedro

55, Grove Road. Tel: (0323) 25359

Cats Whiskers Restaurant

4, Cornfield Terrace. Tel: (0323) 31309

Charles Dickens Restaurant

15, Silverdale Road. Tel: (0323) 643269

Charlie Browns Diner

26a, Susans Road. Tel: (0323) 26588

Chez Dupree

48, Grove Road. Tel: (0323) 24637

The Cloister Restaurant

113, Seaside Road. Tel: (0323) 24761

Corros Restaurant

Compton Street. BN21 4AN Tel: (0323) 645188

The Court House Restaurant

Star Road. Tel: (0323) 642920

Crimples Restaurant

42/44, Meads Street. Tel: (0323) 26805

Crumbles Coffee Lounge

2, Susans Road. Tel: (0323) 26162

The Curry House Restaurant

63, Seaside Road. Tel: (0323) 34608

Dallas

8, Susans Road. Tel: (0323) 22451

The Drive
153, Victoria Drive. Tel: (0323) 29291

Due Scalini
124, Seaside Road. Tel: (0323) 35425

Dukes Restaurant
8, Hyde Gardens. Tel: (0323) 645612

Emerald Chinese Restaurant
42, Seaside. Tel: (0323) 638667

The Golden Phoenix Restaurant
245, Terminus Road. Tel: (0323) 20300

Good Friend Restaurant
95, Cavendish Place. Tel: (0323) 22106

The Grosvenor Grill
67, Grove Road. Tel: (0323) 20914

Hills Restaurant
24, Seaside. Tel: (0323) 32616

The Holiday Inn
7, Carlisle Road. Tel: (0323) 32481

Hotel Mandalay and Restaurant
16, Trinity Trees. Tel: (0323) 29222

The Indian Palace Tandoori Restaurant
54, Seaside Road. BN21 3PB Tel: (0323) 37483

Indian Paradise
166, Seaside. Tel: (0323) 35408

The Indian Paradise Tandoori Restaurant
166, Seaside. Tel: (0323) 35408

The Inn on the Track
Terminus Road. Tel: (0323) 26236

Jays Restaurant
4, Bolton Road. Tel: (0323) 31053

The Jolly Roger Restaurant
42, Seaside Road. Tel: (0323) 21749

Jungles Restaurant
20, The Mall. Tel: (0323) 38155

Justins Bistro
9, Compton Street. Tel: (0323) 22828

Krishna Brasserie
11, Seaside. Tel: (0323) 410339

La Bonne Cuisine Italian Restaurant
40, Ocklynge Road. Tel: (0323) 24687

La Buca Italian Bistro
68, Susans Road. Tel: (0323) 20252

La Lupa Italian Restaurant
213, Terminus Road. Tel: (0323) 21640

La Taverna
92, Seaside. Tel: (0323) 23240

Le Jardin Restaurant
18, Prideaux Road. Tel: (0323) 642291

Lilac
7, Carlisle Buildings. Tel: (0323) 31352

Luigis Italian Restaurant
72, Seaside Road. Tel: (0323) 36994

The Maharaja Restaurant
6, Susans Road. Tel: (0323) 32889

The Master Fryer
29, Langney Road. Tel: (0323) 20170

McDonalds
Arndale Centre. Tel: (0323) 645469

Mister Pickwick Restaurant
226, Terminus Road. Tel: (0323) 22258

Molly's Pantry
22, Willingdon Road. Tel: (0323) 28696

Mr Hau of Eastbourne
219, Terminus Road. Tel: (0323) 23723

Natures Way Restaurant
196, Terminus Road. Tel: (0323) 643211

The New Inn
Grange Road. Tel: (0323) 35363

The New Mum Tajmahal
76, Seaside. Tel: (0323) 21088

Nicholangelo's
89, South Street. Tel: (0323) 21830

The Oak Cabin Restaurant
169, Terminus Road. Tel: (0323) 20833

The Pizza Piazza
4, Pevensey Road. Tel: (0323) 410312

The Pizza Place
57 Terminus Road, Arndale Centre. Tel: (0323) 22780

The Porthole Restaurant
8, Cornfield Terrace. Tel: (0323) 20767/638852

Prescott's
50, Meads Street. Tel: (0323) 646590

The Princess Restaurant
25, Seaside Road. Tel: (0323) 20002

The Retreat Restaurant
10, North Street. Tel: (0323) 647991

Rumblebelly Restaurant
5, Seaside Road. Tel: (0323) 28247

Seeracha
94, Seaside. Tel: (0323) 642867/30502

Shades Restaurant
3 - 5, Bolton Road. Tel: (0323) 641718

Sherry's Restaurant
124, Seaside Road. Tel: (0323) 35425

Spartan Restaurant
48, Grove Road. Tel: (0323) 24637

Susans Cafe
15, Pevensey Road. Tel: (0323) 31893

Sussex Fish Restaurant
39/41, Seaside Road. Tel: (0323) 20387

Taj Mahal Restaurant
23, Seaside. Tel: (0323) 21272

Taurus Steak House
197, Terminus Road. Tel: (0323) 20986

Taylors Restaurant
33, Seaside Road. Tel: (0323) 21793

The Thistle Patisserie
146, Seaside. Tel: (0323) 32365

Toby Carving Room
153, Victoria Drive. Tel: (0323) 29291

True Light
75, Langley Road. Tel: (0323) 24051/644109

Turners Restaurant
1, Cavendish Place. Tel: (0323) 410307

Wimpy Restaurant
37, Terminus Road. Tel: (0323) 20414

Yum Sing Restaurant
3, Carlisle Road. Tel: (0323) 28843/21074

Zodiak Greek Restaurant
240, Terminus Road. Tel: (0323) 25699

PUBLIC HOUSES

The Alexandra Arms
Seaside. Tel: (0323) 20913

The Archery Tavern
346, Seaside. Tel: (0323) 22069

The Beach
74, Beach Road. Tel: (0323) 23542

The Black Horse Inn
220, Seaside. Tel: (0323) 23143

The Bourne Inn
Pevensey Road. Tel: (0323) 24882

The Buccaneer
10, Compton Street. Tel: (0323) 32829

Butler's Free House
7, Bolton Road. Tel: (0323) 646484

Cavalier Inn
13, Carlisle Road. Tel: (0323) 22307

The Crown Inn
22, Crown Street. Tel: (0323) 21160

Devonshire Hotel
96, Seaside Road. Tel: (0323) 31432

The Dolphin
14, South Street. Tel: (0323) 23788

The Eagle Hotel
South Street. Tel: (0323) 23017

Gildredge
17, Terminus Road. Tel: (0323) 32482

The Golden Lion
Arndale Centre. Tel: (0323) 24600

The Hurst Arms
76, Willingdon Road. Tel: (0323) 21762

The Kingfisher
Langney Shopping Precinct, Langney. Tel: (0323) 765004

The Kings Arms
222, Seaside. Tel: (0323) 20361

The Lamb Inn
High Street. Tel: (0323) 20545

The Lion Inn
Marine Parade. Tel: (0323) 26171

The Lodge Inn

559, Seaside . Tel: (0323) 23889

The Lottbridge Arms
Mountfield Road, Hamden Park. Tel: (0323) 503310

The Ocean Wave
29, Latimer Road. Tel: (0323) 33379

The Parkfield
Lindfield Road. Tel: (0323) 502807

The Pilot
Meads Street. Tel: (0323) 23440

The Prince Albert
High Street. Tel: (0323) 27754

The Prince Of Wales
12, Seaside Road. Tel: (0323) 22310

Raglans Bar
6, Bolton Road. Tel: (0323) 34900

Rodmill
1, Rangemore Drive. Tel: (0323) 31784

The Rutland Arms
59, Rutland Road. Tel: (0323) 39308

The Ship
Meads Street. Tel: (0323) 33815

Tally Ho
Church Street. Tel: (0323) 32083

The White Hart Hotel
170, Seaside. Tel: (0323) 25195

The Windsor Tavern
165, Langley Road. Tel: (0323) 26206

CAFÉS & TEA ROOMS

Beach Cafe & Restaurant
56, Beach Road. Tel: (0323) 27262

The Candy Box
24, Meads Street. Tel: (0323) 32372

The Cappuccino
15, Langley Road. Tel: (0323) 24241

Chatsworth Coffee Lounge
5 Chatsworth Walk , 17 Cornfield Road.
Tel: (0323) 26169

Compton Tea Lounge
12, Grand Hotel Buildings. Tel: (0323) 31662

The Conservatory Coffee Lounge
169, Terminus Road. Tel: (0323) 639177

Dayvilles Ice Cream
7, Seaside. Tel: (0323) 641906

Dickens Tea Cottage
5, South Street. Tel: (0323) 32637

O. A. Forte
191, Terminus Road. Tel: (0323) 26994

Hampden Park Cafe
Hampden Park , Hampden Park Road.
Tel: (0323) 502492

The Holywell Tea Chalet
Seafront. Tel: (0323) 33992

Lords Cafe
11, Pevensey Road. Tel: (0323) 35004

Macari's Ice Cream Parlour
246, Terminus Road. Tel: (0323) 24075

Medina Cafe
129, Seaside. Tel: (0323) 26601

Notarianni Bros
203, Terminus Road. Tel: (0323) 23332

Peg's Pantry
12, Winston Crescent. Tel: (0323) 23829

The Plantation Coffee Shop & Restaurant
39, Cornfield Road. Tel: (0323) 27296

The Redoubt Cafe
Off Redoubt Road. Tel: (0323) 33598

The Rendevous Cafe
5 Brassey Avenue , Hamden Park. Tel: (0323) 509577

Rosylee Cafe
379, Seaside. Tel: (0323) 24874

Stage Door Coffee Shop
11, Carlisle Road. Tel: (0323) 37399

Teresa Fusciardi
30, Marine Parade. Tel: (0323) 21128

The Upper Crust
42, Terminus Road. Tel: (0323) 37444

Wish Tower Cafe
King Edward Parade. Tel: (0323) 28685

OTHER AMENITIES

ART GALLERIES
Britannia Watercolour
1 Milton Grange , Arundel Road. Tel: (0323) 38181

Eastbourne Fine Art
9, Meads Street. Tel: (0323) 25634

Penns Gallery
41a, South Street. Tel: (0323) 25204

Picture Palace
228, Terminus Road. Tel: (0323) 35368

Premier Gallery
24-26, South Street. Tel: (0323) 36023

E. Stacy-Marks
24, Cornfield Road. Tel: (0323) 20429/32653

Stewart Gallery
25, Grove Road. Tel: (0323) 29588

BOAT HIRE
Allchorn Bros
63, Channel View Road. Tel: (0323) 34701

BUS & COACH SERVICES
Southdown Motor Services
32, Cavendish Place. Tel: (0323) 27354

CAR HIRE
A. B. C. Auto Hire
59, Enys Road. Tel: (0323) 21683

Car Comfort Hire
Marine Road. Tel: (0323) 30636

Crown Cars
198, Seaside. Tel: (0323) 640082

East Dean Motors
28 -29, Commercial Road. Tel: (0323) 20681

Eastbourne Town Radio Cars
15, North Street. Tel: (0323) 25335

Elite Chauffeur Hire
9, Hardy Drive. Tel: (0323) 640003

D. J. Hodgeton
8 - 9 Walden Mews, Meads Street. Tel: (0323) 645266

Imperial Motors
3 - 5, Susans Road. Tel: (0323) 648484

Lamb's Of Eastbourne
31, The Goffs. Tel: (0323) 643902

Meads Auto Car Hire
De Walden Garage , Meads Street. Tel: (0323) 30628

R. T. L. Enterprises
R. T. L. House, Sutton Road. Tel: (0323) 642955

Rolls Royce Hire
Walden Mews , Meads Street. Tel: (0323) 645266

Skinners
Hammonds Drive, Lottbridge Drive. Tel: (0323) 647141

CINEMAS
The Curzon Cinema
Langley Road. Tel: (0323) 411169

GARDEN CENTRES
B & Q Garden & DIY Centre
Marshall Road, off Lottbridge Drive. Tel: (0323) 509466

Glyndley Nurseries
Hailsham Road , Stone Cross. Tel: (0323) 763240

Stone Cross Nurseries
Rattle Road , Stone Cross. Tel: (0323) 763250

Willingdon Garden Centre
197, Willingdon Road. Tel: (0323) 503455

HEALTH CLUBS
Eastbourne Health Studio
32, Pevensey road. Tel: (0323) 24189

Kingscott Health Clinic 87
87, Terminus Road. Tel: (0323) 29334/729818

HOSPITALS
All Saints Hospital
King Edward Parade. Tel: (0323) 20106

Eastbourne District General Hospital
Kings Drive. Tel: (0323) 21351
Princess Alice Memorial Hospital
Carew Road. Tel: (0323) 22744
St. Mary's Hospital
Church Street. Tel: (0323) 20662

HOSTEL
Youth Hostels Association
East Dean Road. Tel: (0323) 21081/21225

LEISURE CENTRES
Cavendish Sport Centre
Eldon Road. Tel: (0323) 647683
Malt House Leisure Centre
2, Pevensey Road. Tel: (0323) 31871
Sundowners Leisure Centre
Pevensey By Road . Tel: (0323) 762459

NIGHT CLUBS
Caleb's Night Club
18, Langley Road. Tel: (0323) 644848
Raffles
43, Seaside Road. Tel: (0323) 643268
Tuxedo Junction
146/8, Terminus Road. Tel: (0323) 23456

RAILWAY STATION
Hamden Park Station
Station Approach, Brassey Avenue. Tel: (0323) 502020

SNOOKER CENTRES
Malthouse Snooker Club
18, Langney Road. Tel: (0323) 22493
Q-Ball Snooker Club
126, Seaside. Tel: (0323) 24995

STORES
Army & Navy Stores
177, Terminus Road. Tel: (0323) 27663/20416
BHS Plc
Unit 3, Arndale Centre. Tel: (0323) 642836
Brighton Co-Operative Society
202, Terminus Road. Tel: (0323) 20471
Debenhams
152/170, Terminus Road. Tel: (0323) 21321
Littlewoods
49, Arndale Centre. Tel: (0323) 643361
Marks & Spencer plc
133, Terminus Road. Tel: (0323) 648431

SWIMMING POOL
Eastbourne Leisure Pool

Royal Parade. Tel: (0323) 22567

TAXIS
Ace Taxis
26a, Seaside Road. Tel: (0323) 641336
Carlton Carriage
Studio 5, Wish Road. Tel: (0323) 644361
Centre Car Taxi Services
20a, Susans Road. Tel: (0323) 37788
Eastbourne & Country Taxi Service
Old Orchard Road. Tel: (0323) 27766
Eastbourne Station Taxis
Eastbourne Station , Terminus Road. Tel: (0323) 25511
Greyhound Taxi
Railway Station, Terminus Road. Tel: (0323) 20384
Radio Cars
15, North Street. Tel: (0323) 35566
Ranks
Eastbourne Station. Tel: (0323) 25511

THEATRE
The Tivoli Performing Arts Centre
111, Seaside Road. Tel: (0323) 644402
Tourist Information Centre
Royal Parade. Tel: (0323) 645057

WINE BARS
Bilbo Baggins Wine Bar
53, South Street. Tel: (0323) 21713
Bodega
6, Church Street . Tel: (0323) 25503

ZOO
Butterfly Centre
Royal Parade. Tel: (0323) 645522

❧ ❧ ❧ ❧ ❧ ❧ ❧

ETCHINGHAM
At the confluence of the Rother and Dudwell rivers. The Rother was navigable as far as here in the Middle Ages, and the present commuter station was the site of the stronghold of the de Echyngham family. The present church of The Assumption and St. Nicholas was completed by Sir William de Echyngham just before he died in 1388. He is commemorated, headless, on a brass.
Population: 666.

PLACES OF INTEREST
Haremere Hall
Tel: (058 081) 245
An early 17th century Manor house with Minstrel staircase, panelled Great Hall and Flemish Fireplace. Collec-

HAREMERE HALL, ETCHINGHAM

tion of rugs, ornaments pottery plate from Middle and Far East. Period furniture.

Months Open: Gardens: Easter - October. House: by appointment. Days Open: Everyday. Hours Open: 2 - 5pm. Bank Holidays: House only. Admission: £2.50. Opera Festival and Christmas breaks

HOTEL
De De Etchingham Arms
High Street. Tel: (058 081) 292

OTHER AMENITY
TOURS & SIGHTS
Sussex Shire Horses
The Stables, Haremere Hall. Tel: (058 081) 501

🐾 🐾 🐾 🐾 🐾 🐾 🐾

EWHURST
Lying close on the Kent border and overlooked by Bodiam Castle, this once remote village has been extensively gentrified.
Population: 883.

HOTEL
The White Dog Inn
Village Green. Tel: (058 083) 264

OTHER AMENITY
CARAVAN PARK
Lordine Court Caravan Park
Lordine Lane. Tel: (058 083) 209

🐾 🐾 🐾 🐾 🐾 🐾 🐾

FAIRLIGHT
Just east of Hastings, centred around a collection of old coastguards cottages. The 'Lovers' Seat' at Fairlight Cove, has been moved back from it original spot on the unstable cliff edge. This is where a

certain Captain Lamb of Rye, scaled the cliffs to meet his beloved Miss Boys. Her parents banished her to Fairlight in the hope of breaking what they considered to be an unsuitable match. Legend has it that they finally relented and gave their consent to the union. The founder of the opera company, Richard D'Oyly Carte, is buried in the churchyard of St Andrew's, that is in a wonderful poition.
Population: 1,447.

HOTELS
Fairlight Cove Hotel
Waites Lane. TN35 4AX. Tel: (0424) 812209
Fairlight Lodge Hotel
Martineau Lane. Tel: (0424) 812104

RESTAURANTS
Castro's Spanish Restaurant
Coastguard Lane. Tel: (0424) 812387
Crossways Licensed Restaurant
Pett Level Road. Tel: (0424) 812356

🐾 🐾 🐾 🐾 🐾 🐾 🐾

FAIRWARP
Situated at the southern tip of the Ashdown Forest, an attractive place with a backdrop of pine trees and the church which is Victorian, having been completed in 1881.

PUBLIC HOUSE
Forester's Arms
Tel: (082 571) 2808

🐾 🐾 🐾 🐾 🐾 🐾 🐾

FALMER
The village has obviously been transformed latterly by being home to the University of Sussex. The campus architecture is worth a glimpse.
Population: 165.

PLACES OF INTEREST
Gardner Centre for the Arts
Set within the university campus but open to the public, the centre houses an excellent theatre and a small exhibition gallery.

PUBLIC HOUSE
The Swan Inn
Middle Street. Tel: (0273) 681842

🐾 🐾 🐾 🐾 🐾 🐾 🐾

CHARLESTON FARM HOUSE

FELBRIDGE

Now little more than a road junction on the A 22 north of East Grinstead, this was once the site of an important coaching stop. The garage opposite the inn began life as a smithy, and is still with the same family firm.

HOTEL
Toads Croak House
30 Copthorne Road. RH19 2NS. Tel: (0342) 328524

RESTAURANTS
Happy Eater Restaurant
Star Inn. Tel: (0342) 325441/321026
The Woodcock
Woodcock Hill. Tel: (0342) 325859

PUBLIC HOUSE
The Star Inn
London Road. Tel: (0342) 323239
OTHER AMENITIES
CAR HIRE/SELF DRIVE
Woodcock Motors Ltd.
St. Marys, Woodcock Hill. Tel: (0342) 326470/314668
Woods Car & Van Rental

Sidlow Garage, London Road. Tel: (0342) 311616

GARDEN CENTRE
Cramphorn plc
Copthorne Road. Tel: (0342) 328881

ᘓ ᘓ ᘓ ᘓ ᘓ ᘓ ᘓ

FIRLE

The home of the English greengage. Thomas Gage of Firle Place was responsible for introducing it to this country.
Population: 273.

PLACES OF INTEREST
Charleston Farm House (above)
Tel: (032 183) 265
Something of Bloomsbury-by-the-Sea. This was the home of Virginia Woolf's sister Vanessa, her sons Julian and Quentin Bell, painter Duncan Grant and writer David Garnett; it is now a museum (some would say a shrine) to their life style. There is a heady atmosphere about the house that is both infectious and inspiring. Well worth a visit.
Months Open: April - October. Days Open: Wednesday -

DUNCAN GRANT'S STUDIO, CHARLESTON FARM HOUSE

Sunday. Hours Open: 2-6pm (last entry 5pm). Bank Holidays: Open.

Firle Beacon

At 718 feet above sea level, this high spot offers a wonderful view of central and east Sussex and, on a clear day, into Kent, some thirty miles away.

Firle Place

Tel: (079 159) 335

The original Tudor house was altered about 1730. Home of the Gage family since the 15th century. The house contains an important collection of English and European pictures. *Months Open: June - September. Days Open: Wednesdays, Thursday and Sundays. Bank Holidays: Open Easter, Spring, May, Summer. Cold buffet luncheon. Sussex cream teas.*

PUBLIC HOUSE

The Ram Inn

Tel: (079 159) 222

🐾 🐾 🐾 🐾 🐾 🐾 🐾

FIVE ASH DOWN

On the A 26, slightly north west of Maresfield, in what was Ashdown Forest.

PUBLIC HOUSE

The Firemans Arms

Tel: (082 581) 2191

🐾 🐾 🐾 🐾 🐾 🐾 🐾

FIVE ASHES

PUBLIC HOUSE

Five Ashes Inn

Tel: (082 585) 485

OTHER AMENITY

HEALTH CLUB
Five Ashes Gym

Boltons Clinic, Leeds Lane. Tel: (082 585) 447

FLETCHING

Famous in the Middle Ages for its arrow heads, although the name has apparently nothing to do with 'fletching', making arrows, but is derived from the Saxon. This is where Simon de Montfort's army camped before the battle of Lewes in 1264, and he kept vigil in the church. The fact that de Montfort routed King Henry III's army was taken by moralists of the time to prove the power of prayer. Edward Gibbon, author of 'The Decline and Fall of the Roman Empire' is buried in the churchyard.

Population: 863.

PUBLIC HOUSES

The Griffin Inn

Tel: (082 572) 2890

Rose & Crown

Tel: (082 572) 2039

🐾 🐾 🐾 🐾 🐾 🐾 🐾

FLIMWELL

Right on the Kent border, some three miles west of Hawkhurst. St Augustine's is a Victorian church.

HOTELS

Hare & Hounds Hotel

Tel: (058 087) 321

Postboys Motel

Hastings Road. Tel: (058 087) 494

RESTAURANTS

Happy Eater Restaurants

A21, Hastings Road. Tel: (0892) 890547

Mr Eats Diner

London Road. Tel: (058 087) 600

Woods Licenced Restaurant

High Street. Tel: (058 087) 342

PUBLIC HOUSE

The Royal Oak Public House

London Road. Tel: (058 087) 320

🐾 🐾 🐾 🐾 🐾 🐾 🐾

FOREST ROW

Ashdown is the forest in question, and this village marks its western tip. William Cobbet thought it 'a pretty village'. The tile-hung old coaching inn, the Chequers, is older than the church. A stone in the wall of the village hall celebrates a visit by President Kennedy.

Population: 4,245.

PLACES OF INTEREST

Kidbrooke Park

Built in 1730 with later alterations. Sandstone house and stables.

Months Open: August. Days Open: Everyday. Hours Open: 9am - 6pm. Bank Holidays: May only.

HOTELS

Brambletye Hotel

The Square, Lewes Road. RH18 5EZ. Tel: (034 282) 4144/4145

The Chequers Inn

The Square, Lewes Road. Tel: (034 282) 3333/4394

PUBLIC HOUSES

The Foresters Arms

Hartfield Road. Tel: (034 282) 2792

The Hatch Inn

Colemans Hatch. Tel: (034 282) 2363

CAFÉ/TEA ROOMS

Table Talk

1 Ashorne House, Lewes Road. Tel: (034 282) 3530

OTHER AMENITIES

HEALTH CLUB

Gaia Natural Therapies

London Road. Tel: (034 282) 2716

Natural health clinic and herbal apothecary

Months Open: All year. Days Open: Mon-Sat. Hours Open: Clinic 8.00-6.00 Apothecary 10.00-5.00. Not open on Bank Holidays. Drive in off the A22, park in our own car park and step into the past as you enter our herbal apothecary. Let our friendly staff weigh you out healing herbs and advise you on the right blend for your cough or digestive problem. Enjoy the scents of lavender and jasmine as you test our essential oils and order a bath oil or massage oil mixed to your own specifications. We also sell vitamins, books, crystals and natural cosmetics. Proprietor: Donald Cartwright

TAXI

Forest Cars

3 Grosvenor Road. Tel: (034 282) 3998

🐾 🐾 🐾 🐾 🐾 🐾 🐾

FRAMFIELD

Some two and a half miles west of Uckfield. The nearby road called 'Terrible Down' is reputedly the site of a battle long forgotten by the history books. Folklore has it that the fighters plodded through blood up to their knees.

Population: 1,930.

HOTEL

Bay Trees Hotel & Restaurant

The Street. Tel: (082 582) 818/636

PUBLIC HOUSES

The Barley Mow

Eastbourne Road. Tel: (082 582) 234

Hare & Hounds

The Street. Tel: (082 582) 327

🐾 🐾 🐾 🐾 🐾 🐾 🐾

FRANT

South of Tunbridge Wells, but within East Sussex. The village developed rapidly in the railway age, with many Victorian and neo-Georgian commuter houses being built. The station, more than a mile distant, is a tiny jewel of Victorian railway architecture.

Population: 1,357.

RESTAURANT

Bassetts Restaurant

37 High Street. Tel: (089 275) 635

🐾 🐾 🐾 🐾 🐾 🐾 🐾

GLYNDE

Glynde goes back almost to 'Doomsday' but is now most justly famous for the Glyndebourne Opera founded by John Christie.

Population: 200.

PLACES OF INTEREST

Glynde Place

Tel: (079 159) 337

Dating from the 1560s, the Morley family had this house built when they outgrew Glyndebourne. Pictures, Bronzes and historical documents. Beautiful example of 16th century architecture.

Months Open: June - September. Days Open: Wednesdays and Thursday, first & last Sundays of month. Hours Open: 2.15 - 5.30pm. Bank Holidays: Easter Sunday and Monday . Admission: £2.20. Children £1.00. Home baked teas

Glyndebourne

The original house was much extended in the Victorian period. The opera house situated by the main house was opened in 1934.

PUBLIC HOUSE

Trevor Arms

The Street. Tel: (079 159) 208

GLYNDEBOURNE

OTHER AMENITY
THEATRE
Glyndebourne Opera House
Tel: (0273) 812321

🐦 🐦 🐦 🐦 🐦 🐦 🐦

GOLDEN CROSS
Situated at a crossroads on the East Hoathly to Hailsham road.

RESTAURANT
The Golden Horse
BN27 4AJ Tel: (0825) 872230

PUBLIC HOUSES
Deanland Tavern
Deanland Wood Park. Tel: (0825) 872406
Golden Cross Inn
Tel: (0825) 872216

OTHER AMENITIES
CARAVAN PARK - RESIDENTIAL
Deanland Wood Park
Tel: (0825) 872359

GARDEN CENTRE
Deanland Nursery
Deanland Road. Tel: (0825) 872509

🐦 🐦 🐦 🐦 🐦 🐦 🐦

GROOMBRIDGE
Straddling the Kent border, between East Grinstead and Tunbridge Wells. The Sussex side of the town suffers badly from comparison with the Kent side, being created with the coming of the railway, and is in effect New Groombridge.

PLACES OF INTEREST
Dower House
Tel: (0892) 890381

HOTEL
The Crown Inn
The Green. Tel: (0892) 864742

PUBLIC HOUSES
The Huntsman
Eridge Green. Tel: (0892) 864258
The Junction Inn

Station Road. Tel: (0892) 864275
The Victoria Inn
Withyham Road. Tel: (0892) 864206

OTHER AMENITY
TAXI
Kandy Kars
2 Lyons Villas, Station Road. Tel: (0892) 864212

🐾 🐾 🐾 🐾 🐾 🐾 🐾

GUESTLING
The original meeting place of 'the Court Guestling', the governing body of the Cinque Ports. The isolated church of St Laurence is Saxon in origin.
Population: 1,332.

HOTEL
White Hart Inn
Winchelsea Road. Tel: (0424) 813187

PUBLIC HOUSE
The Three Oaks
Butchers Lane. Tel: (0424) 813303

OTHER AMENITIES
CARAVAN PARK
Old Coghurst Farm
Rock Lane. Tel: (0424) 753622

GARDEN CENTRE
Harborough Nurseries
The Thorne. Tel: (0424) 814220

HOSTEL
Youth Hostels Association
Guestling Hall. Tel: (0424) 812373

🐾 🐾 🐾 🐾 🐾 🐾 🐾

HADLOW
The remarkable 170 foot folly tower that dominates the Medway plain is all that remains of Hadlow Castle. It was built by one Walter Barton May, reputedly to keep an eye on his errant wife, and was used by the Royal Observer Corps in the Second World War. The town is an attractive collection of brick and weatherboard houses and a medieval church.
Population: 941.

PUBLIC HOUSE
New Inn
Main Road. Tel: (082 585) 209

OTHER AMENITY
RIDING SCHOOL
Canters End Riding School
Canters End, Main Road. TN22 4HP Tel: (082 585) 213

🐾 🐾 🐾 🐾 🐾 🐾 🐾

HAILSHAM
A small market town, with one of the largest and most important cattle markets in Sussex. During the boom in meat prices in 1973 the surrounding area was the centre of an outbreak of rustling. One of the town's older industries is rope making, and they even supplied HM Prisons with rope for executions. The High Street has some fine Georgian buildings, and there is a modern shopping precinct.
Population: 12,681.

PLACES OF INTEREST
Leaning House
Once an inn, the Leaning House now has a one-roomed museum devoted to a cottage history of the area.

HOTELS
The Old Forge Hotel and Restaurant
Magham Down. Tel: (0323) 842893
Terminus Hotel
Station Road. Tel: (0323) 843603

RESTAURANTS
The Cottage Restaurant
Polegate Road. Tel: (0323) 847216
Hong Kong House
14, Vicarage Road. Tel: (0323) 843549
The Pizza Platta
5b, George Street. Tel: (0323) 440049/440052
Rajdhutt Restaurant
48, High Street. Tel: (0323) 842847
Waldernheath Country Restaurant
Magham Down, Amberstone Corner. Tel: (0323) 840143
English and French Cuisine. Specialities: Roasts, seasonal game, fresh local produce. Own kitchen garden. Hours Open: Lunch: 12.00-2.00. Dinner: 7.00-9.00. Closed First two weeks of January. Open Sundays. Lunch: £ 9.50. Dinner: £ 15.75. House Wine: £ 6.25. Credit Cards: Ac. Am. D. V. Seating Capacity: 45. Outdoor eating. Veg. W/chair acc. B. P. W.

PUBLIC HOUSES
The Bricklayers Arms
Ersham Road. Tel: (0323) 841587
The Crown & Anchor
High Street. Tel: (0323) 843643

The George Hotel
George Street. Tel: (0323) 840144
The Grenadier Hotel
High Street. Tel: (0323) 842152
The Kings Head
South Road. Tel: (0323) 843880
The Railway Tavern
Station Road. Tel: (0323) 482442
The Red Lion
Magham Down. Tel: (0323) 840079

CAFÉS & TEA ROOMS
Genesis Coffee Bar
19, Station Road. Tel: (0323) 440822
M.J.M. Bakeries
3, Station Road. Tel: (0323) 846255

OTHER AMENITIES
BUS & COACH SERVICES
Southdown Motor Services
Mill Road. Tel: (0323) 841365

CAR HIRE
Mitchells
South Road. Tel: (0323) 842414
R F Self Drive Hire
1a Sussex Cottages , Magham Down. Tel: (0323) 847116

CARAVAN PARKS
Bakers Farm Park Homes
9, Upper Horsebridge. Tel: (0323) 844495
Godfrey Davies Park Homes
Lion House, Park Mill Road. Tel: (0323) 840059
Sandy Bank Caravan Park
Magham Down. Tel: (0323) 842488

GARDEN CENTRE
Ersham Road Farmshop & Garden Centre
Ersham Road. Tel: (0323) 847066

LEISURE CENTRE
Hailsham Leisure Centre
Vicarage Lane. Tel: (0323) 846755-842944

STORE
Woolworths plc
17, High Street. Tel: (0323) 841671

TAXIS
Bishops Taxis
134, London Road. Tel: (0323) 847405
Brians Taxis
15, Queens Road. Tel: (0323) 833556
Cavalier Cars

Hailsham Market. Tel: (0323) 844464
Centre Car Taxi Services
29 - 30, Vicarage Fields. Tel: (0323) 843180
Crescent Taxis
40 Moore Park, Town Farm. Tel: (0323) 842827
Jayline Taxis
8b, George street. Tel: (0323) 841869
Longley's
Longleaze , Arlington Road. Tel: (0323) 841674

WINE BAR
The Blue Poppy
7, High Street. Tel: (0323) 846616

🐾 🐾 🐾 🐾 🐾 🐾 🐾

HALLAND
A mile and a half west of East Hoathly. Sir John Pelham, whose family badge adorns so many buildings in this part of Sussex, including Halland Park Farm, came from here. The badge was a reward for his part in the capture of King John of France at the Battle of Poitiers in 1356.

PLACES OF INTEREST
Bentley Motor Museum
Tel: (082 584) 711

HOTEL
Halland Forge Hotel & Restaurant
BN8 6PW. Tel: (082 584) 456

PUBLIC HOUSE
The Black Lion
Tel: (082 584) 304

OTHER AMENITY
RIDING SCHOOL
A. Mount
Crockstead Farm. Tel: (082 584) 797

🐾 🐾 🐾 🐾 🐾 🐾 🐾

HARTFIELD
On the edge of Ashdown Forest, a pretty village built around a dog-leg of a main street. It was near here that A. A. Milne lived, and the countryside around about provided the setting for Winnie the Pooh's adventures. The same house was owned by the late Brian Jones, of the Rolling Stones, whose body was found floating in the swimming-pool.
Population: 2,097.

HASTINGS CASTLE

RESTAURANT
Anchor Inn
Church Street. Tel: (0892) 770424

PUBLIC HOUSES
Gallipot Inn
Gallipot Street, Upper Hartfield. Tel: (0892) 770268
Haywagon Inn & Restaurant
High Street. Tel: (0892) 770252

OTHER AMENITIES
RIDING SCHOOLS
Barr Equestrian & Marine Services
Bolebrook Wood Farm, Edenbridge Road. Tel: (0892) 770591
Bolebrook Wood Farm Livery Yard
Edenbridge Road. Tel: (0892) 770591

🐾 🐾 🐾 🐾 🐾 🐾 🐾

HASTINGS
It is appropriate that this ancient port, the premier Cinque Port, should have the most famous battle on English soil named after it. You have to peel away a hundred-year-old outer skin to find the thousand-year-old town, but it is still there with its main street of ancient houses, all skew-whiff. William I established a wooden castle here on a motte, or man-made mound, before marching off to engage Harold in Battle. The remains on Castle Hill are not of that castle, but of the one begun in 1070. The town declined in importance as its topography changed, its port dried up, and half of West Hill was washed away by the storms of 1287 (see Winchelsea and Rye). It is thought that the original Saxon harbour was in the centre of the modern town. With the decline of the port during the middle ages Hastings resorted to fishing, until the seaside resort boom in the 19th century led to the town being recreated, and effectively merged with St Leonard's into a holiday resort, with all the accompanying features, including the obligatory pier. Though the fishing industry is, as everywhere in the country, in decline, the fishing-net sheds, where the nets are hung to be dried, are still in use. The town is still prosperous and expanding, with many attractions for the visitor.
Population: 75,284.

PLACES OF INTEREST
Castle
Half has crumbled into the sea, but there remains an

identifiable ruin. The castle dates from 1069.

Fishermans Museum

The main exhibit is the Enterprise, built in Hastings together with the Capstan. Included in the exhibits is a large picture of the presentation to Sir Winston Churchill of a golden winkle at the Enterprise on Winkle Island in September 1955.

Months Open: May - September. Days Open: Sunday - Friday. Hours Open: 10.30 - 12pm, 2.30 - 5pm; Sundays 3 - 5pm. The last of the old clinker-built sailing luggers built in Hastings.

Hastings Museum and Art Gallery

Johns Place, Cambridge Road.

Tel: (0424) 721202

This museum now houses the admirable collections previously held at the Brassey Institute. Oriental, Pacific and American Indian Art, paintings, ceramics, local natural history and geology.

Months Open: All year. Days Open: Everyday. Hours Open: Mon - Sat, 10am - 1pm, 2 - 5pm. Sun 3 - 5pm.

Museum of Local History

Old Town Hall, High Street.

Displays on local maritime history, the Cinque Ports, smuggling, fishing.

Months Open: Easter - September. Days Open: Monday - Saturday. Hours Open: 10am - 1pm, 2 - 5pm. Bank Holidays: Easter Sunday. Admission: 15p. Children 10p.

Old Town Hall Museum

Tel: (0424) 721209

Shipwreck Heritage Centre

Tel: (0424) 437452

A new museum whose exhibits are from three local wrecks - the warship Anne (1690), the Dutch ship Amsterdam (1749) and a Danish ship (1861). These contain muskets, brandy, wine, and a tombstone. A 15th century wreck is displayed in a sound and light show.

Months Open: March - October. Days Open: Daily May - September, weekends other times. Admission: £1.00. Children 75p. Large car and coach park.

HOTELS

Ambassador Hotel & Restaurant

1 East Parade. Tel: (0424) 430677

Beechwood Hotel (right)

59 Baldslow Road. Tel: (0424) 420078

BEDROOMS: 3 single B&B £ 12.00 - £ 23.00. 3 Double, (1 en suite) B&B £ 22.00 - £ 35.00. 2 Twin, (1 en suite) B&B £ 30.00 - £ 35.00. RESTAURANT: English Cuisine. HOTEL INFORMATION: CF. W.

Chatsworth Hotel

Carlisle Parade. Tel: (0424) 423074

Churchills Hotel

3 St. Helens Crescent. Tel: (0424) 439359

The Cinque Ports Hotel

Summerfield, Bohemia Road. Tel: (0424) 439222

D'Arcy Hall Hotel

White Rock Gardens. Tel: (0424) 425774

French's

24 Robertson Street. Tel: (0424) 421195

Gainsborough Hotel

5 Carlisle Parade. Tel: (0424) 434010

Close to sea and all amenities. Bedrooms have TV and tea and coffee making facilities, most with sea views and bathrooms en suite.

Imperial Hotel

119 Queens Road. Tel: (0424) 435465

Lansdowne Hotel

1 Robertson Terrace. Tel: (0424) 429605

Lindum Hotel

1a Carlisle Parade. Tel: (0424) 434070

The Manor

114 Manor Road. Tel: (0424) 422697

Parrswood Hotel

2 Carlisle Parade. Tel: (0424) 420027

Queens Hotel

5 Robertson Terrace. TN34 1JG. Tel: (0424) 424167

Waldorf Hotel

4 Carlisle Parade. Tel: (0424) 422185

Yelton Hotel

1-7 White Rock. Tel: (0424) 422240

GUEST HOUSES

Amberlene Guest House

12 Cambridge Gardens. Tel: (0424) 439447

Argyle Guest House

32 Cambridge Gardens. Tel: (0424) 421294

Ashdene Guest House

26 Cambridge Gardens. Tel: (0424) 428625

Cambridge Guest House

18 Cambridge Gardens. Tel: (0424) 712995

Carinya Guest House

9 Braybrooke Terrace. Tel: (0424) 446103

Carlton Guest House

40 White Rock. Tel: (0424) 426899

THE BEECHWOOD HOTEL

Castledene Guest House
23 Devonshire Road. Tel: (0424) 432261

The Crown House
90 High Street. Tel: (0424) 431687

East Kent Guest House
38 White Rock. Tel: (0424) 439291

Glenmore Guest House
37 Cambridge Gardens. Tel: (0424) 432915

Kelrose Guest House
22 Devonshire Road. Tel: (0424) 426430

Kingsley Guest House
103 Baybrooke Road. Tel: (0424) 420338

Lighthouse
358 Old London Road. Tel: (0424) 440649

The London Guest House
1a George Street. Tel: (0424) 426605

J.W. Maynard
10 Cornwallis Terrace. Tel: (0424) 421661

Metro Guest House
31 Cambridge Gardens. Tel: (0424) 421737

Millifont Guest House
9 Cambridge Gardens. Tel: (0424) 425645

The Owls Nest
37 Devonshire Road. Tel: (0424) 440863

Regency Guest House
25 Cambridge Gardens. Tel: (0424) 426694

G.G. Rolph
97 Fairlight Road. Tel: (0424) 717181

The Senlac Guest House
47 Cambridge Gardens. Tel: (0424) 430080

White Rock Guest House
28a White Rock. Tel: (0424) 435310

RESTAURANTS

Blue Dolphin Fish & Chips
61b High Street. Tel: (0424) 425778

Caesars Restaurant
9 George Street. Tel: (0424) 429211

Castle Tandoori Restaurant
43 George Street. Tel: (0424) 429685

Chop Suey House
286 Priory Road. Tel: (0424) 431983

Coach House Restaurant
60a All Saints Street. Tel: (0424) 428080

Curry Garden Tandoori
362 Old London Road. TN35 5BB Tel: (0424) 445268

Dallas Burger Bar
39 Robertson Street. Tel: (0424) 427830

The Dining Room
63 George Street. Tel: (0424) 434960

Dishes of the World
208 Queens Road. Tel: (0424) 431420

Emiliana
219 Harold Road. Tel: (0424) 434341

Erol's Kebab & Steak House
194 Queens Road. Tel: (0424) 422418

Fagin's Restaurant
73 George Street. Tel: (0424) 439319

Flynns Restaurant
26 White Rock. Tel: (0424) 423579

The Golden Boat
443 Old London Road. Tel: (0424) 439441

Happy House
75 Vicarage Road. Tel: (0424) 445890

The Harbour Restaurant
1 East Beach Street. Tel: (0424) 425558

Hastings Castle Restaurant
10 Pelham Arcade. Tel: (0424) 429789

Hobdens
29 George Street. Tel: (0424) 425786

Hughenden Fishbar
9 Hughenden Road. Tel: (0424) 428574

Hunky Burgers
8 Rock-a-Nore Road, Old Town. Tel: (0424) 437216

The Italian Way
25 Castle Street. Tel: (0424) 435955

Kentucky Fried Chicken
5 York Buildings, Wellington Place. Tel: (0424) 434040

Lavender & Lace
106 All Saints Street, Old Town. Tel: (0424) 716290

Le Flacon Restaurant
24 White Rock. Tel: (0424) 439089

Lifeboat Restaurant
14 East Parade. Tel: (0424) 420388

Lord Sam Old Town Bistro
61 George Street, Old Town. TN34 3EE Tel: (0424) 446104

The Lunch Box
17 Claremont. Tel: (0424) 427997

Maggie's Restaurant
4 Trinity Street. Tel: (0424) 430933

K. Matheou
68 Mount Pleasant Road. Tel: (0424) 431034

Mermaid Restaurant
2 Rock-a-Nore Road. Tel: (0424) 438100

Micky's Restaurant
51a Robertson Street. Tel: (0424) 429030

Mings Restaurant
17 Grand Parade. Tel: (0424) 442230

Mr Chippys
78 Queens Road. Tel: (0424) 432823

Muktha Restaurant
75 Queens Road. Tel: (0424) 714210/445007

Munchies Take-Away
284 Priory Road. Tel: (0424) 439607

New Hong Kong Kitchen
211 Harold Road. Tel: (0424) 439350

Orange Tree Restaurant
4 Claremont. Tel: (0424) 429910

Perfect Pizza
46 Robertson Street. Tel: (0424) 426832
Promenade Fish Bar & Restaurant
11 Marine Parade. Tel: (0424) 433382
Rainbow Restaurant
11 Sturdee Place. Tel: (0424) 421699
Regal Restaurant
6 East Parade. Tel: (0424) 441474
Restaurant 27
27 George Street. Tel: (0424) 420060
Retsinas Taverna
5 Bank Buildings. Tel: (0424) 430883
Rising Sun
18a East Parade. Tel: (0424) 420248
The Robert de Mortain
373 The Ridge. TN34 2RD Tel: (0424) 751061
Sabar
15 Whitefriars Road. Tel: (0424) 720134
Seagate Restaurant
3 East Parade. Tel: (0424) 424811
Seagull Restaurant
7 East Parade. Tel: (0424) 436151
Seaview Take Away
4 West View. Tel: (0424) 440964
Seven Seas Fish Bar
27 Waldegrave Street. Tel: (0424) 444135
Shiplu Tandoori
177a Queens Road. Tel: (0424) 439493/721991
Spud-U-Like
7 York Buildings, Wellington Place. Tel: (0424) 426705
Sun Wah
6 Claremont. Tel: (0424) 429629
Swan Chop Suey Fish & Chip Bar
168 Queens Road. Tel: (0424) 437160
The Takeaway
2 Sturdee Place. Tel: (0424) 432583
The Town House
3 Marine Parade. Tel: (0424) 438487
Wedges Bistro
18/20 Prospect Place. Tel: (0424) 445706
White Tower Restaurant
35 Robertson Street. Tel: (0424) 427127
The Willow Room
84 All Saints Street. Tel: (0424) 430656
Woodpecker Bistro
36 High Street. Tel: (0424) 434357
Yum Yum Pizza Restaurant
207 Harold Road. Tel: (0424) 424809

PUBLIC HOUSES
The Angel Inn
1 St. Mary's Terrace. Tel: (0424) 433328
Ashburnhams Arms
104 Ashburnham Road. Tel: (0424) 420649

Carlisle Hotel
24 Pelham Street. Tel: (0424) 420193/720470
The Cask & Kettle
27 Havelock Road. Tel: (0424) 421429
Cinque Port Arms
105 All Saints Street. Tel: (0424) 430289
The Clarence Hotel
57 Middle Street. Tel: (0424) 437880
The Clown
9 Russell Street. Tel: (0424) 423623
The Cricketers
31 Weldegrave Street, South Terrace. Tel: (0424) 425086
The Crown Inn
64 All Saints Street, Old Town. Tel: (0424) 428308
Cutter Public House
East Parade. Tel: (0424) 423449
Dolphin Inn
Rock-a-Nore Road. Tel: (0424) 431197
The Dripping Well
1 Dorset Place. Tel: (0424) 421686
The Duke of Wellington
28/29 High Street. Tel: (0424) 431996
The Golden Hind
18 Havelock Road. Tel: (0424) 442406
Granville Hotel
St. Georges Road. Tel: (0424) 429044
The Harrow Inn
Baldslow Down. Tel: (0424) 751109
Hastings Arms
2 George Street. Tel: (0424) 722208
The Jenny Lind
69 High Street. Tel: (0424) 421392
The Kings Head
Court House Street. Tel: (0424) 439292
The Kings Head
71 Rye Road. Tel: (0424) 423767
Langham Hotel
Elphinstone Road. Tel: (0424) 420858
The London Trader
7 East Beach Street. Tel: (0424) 429684
The Lord Nelson
East Bourne Street. Tel: (0424) 423280
The Lord Warden
73 Manor Road. Tel: (0424) 420055
The Malvern
Malvern Way, Broomgrove Estate. Tel: (0424) 430979
The Millers Arms
38 Winchelsea Road. Tel: (0424) 439075
The New Clive Vale
317 Old London Road. Tel: (0424) 426503
Oddfellows Arms
397 Old London Road, West Kingsdown.
Tel: (0424) 423242

Old Golden Cross
56 Havelock Road. Tel: (0424) 721975
The Palace Bars
White Rock. Tel: (0424) 439444
The Prince Albert
Cornwallis Street. Tel: (0424) 425481
The Prince of Wales
15 Western Road. Tel: (0424) 430559
Ye Olde Pump House
64 George Street. Tel: (0424) 422016
The Queen Adelaide
20 West Street. Tel: (0424) 430862
Robert De Mortain
373 The Ridge. Tel: (0424) 751061
The Robin Hood
Sandhurst Road. Tel: (0424) 21383
The Royal Albion
Marine Parade. Tel: (0424) 432658
Royal George
32 Station Road. Tel: (0424) 445603
The Royal Standard
Fishmarket. Tel: (0424) 420163
Royal Sussex Arms
242 Old London Road. Tel: (0424) 432926
The Shah
144 Mount Pleasant Road. Tel: (0424) 439062
The Stag Inn
All Saints Street. Tel: (0424) 425734
Tavern in the Town
Cambridge Road. Tel: (0424) 420074
Town Crier
Queens Road. Tel: (0424) 423324
The Wellington
43 White Rock. Tel: (0424) 424295
The Whitefriars
127 Priory Road. Tel: (0424) 437745

CAFÉS & TEA ROOMS
Baskin-Robbins
The Patio, The Stade. Tel: (0424) 721544
P. Bosworth (Cafe)
1 Cambridge Gardens. Tel: (0424) 422627
Bubbles
2 Claremont. Tel: (0424) 435295
Cafe Royal
5 Castle Street. Tel: (0424) 437793
Dorset Cafe
13 Dorset Place. Tel: (0424) 441599
Jackies Kitchen
111 Cambridge Road. Tel: (0424) 421879
S.M. Legg
Rock-a-Nore Road. Tel: (0424) 439188
Stade Catering
The Patio, The Stade, East Beech Street.

Tel: (0424) 425503
West Hill Cafe
Castle Hill Road. Tel: (0424) 429636
Winchester Cafe
38 George Street. Tel: (0424) 420976
Windmill Cafe
1A Kings Road. Tel: (0424) 425295

OTHER AMENITIES
BUS & COACH SERVICES
Hastings Coaches
Coach Station, Queens Road. Tel: (0424) 722223

CAR HIRE/CHAUFFEUR DRIVEN
S.O.S. Cars
Car Park, Cornwallis Street. Tel: (0424) 421936

CAR HIRE/SELF DRIVE
Estates & Cars
37 Earl Street. Tel: (0424) 720848
Hertz Rent-a-Car
Hollingsworth, Bohemia Road. Tel: (0424) 430745
J.L.S. Self Drive Car Hire
171 Hillside Road. Tel: (0424) 421919
Motorhaven Self Drive Hire
24/28 Winchelsea Road. Tel: (0424) 424445
Swan National Rentals
The Ridge Service Station, The Ridge. Tel: (0424) 428670

CARAVAN PARKS
Gerald Brandon Caravans
Beauport Park, The Ridge West. Tel: (0424) 52807
Rocklands Caravan Park
East Hill. Tel: (0424) 423097
Shearbarn Holiday Park
Barley Lane. Tel: (0424) 423583
Woodlands Park Holiday Homes
Woodlands, Westfield. Tel: (0424) 751696

CINEMA
Cannon Cinema
Queens Road. Tel: (0424) 420517

ENTERTAINMENTS
Hastings Model Village
White Rock. Tel: (0424) 427861
Hastings Pier Company
The Pier. Tel: (0424) 422566
The Stade Putting Course
New Promenade. Tel: (0424) 437227

GARDEN CENTRES
B & Q Garden & DIY Centre
Rye Road. Tel: (0424) 441133

Coghurst Nursery
Ivy House Lane, Nr Three Oaks.
TN35 4NP Tel: (0424) 425371/437657
DIY & Garden Supercentres
Rye Road. Tel: (0424) 441133
Hastings Garden Centre
Bexhill Road. Tel: (0424) 443414/433490
Kenrow
9 St. Helens Park Road. Tel: (0424) 429979
Scollays
400 The Ridge. Tel: (0424) 753072

HEALTH CLUB
Pinks Health Studio
14 Claremont. Tel: (0424) 430566

HOSPITALS
Mount Pleasant Hospital
Frederick Road. Tel: (0424) 720303
Royal East Sussex Hospital
Cambridge Road. Tel: (0424) 434513

LEISURE CENTRES
Hastings Sports Centre
Bohemia Road. Tel: (0424) 722227
West Hill Community Centre
Bembrook Road. Tel: (0424) 420053

NIGHT CLUBS
Dennies
49 Priory Street. Tel: (0424) 428560
Downtown Saturdays
39 George Street. Tel: (0424) 420090/432166
J.R.'s Niteclub
Harold Place. Tel: (0424) 432646
Rumors
53 Robertson Street. Tel: (0424) 444675

RAILWAY STATION
Hastings Miniature Railway
Marine Parade. Tel: (0424) 437440

SKATING RINK
Hastings Ice Rink
Lower Promenade, Sea Front. Tel: (0424) 425731

SNOOKER CENTRE
Victoria Snooker Centre
Wellington Square. Tel: (0424) 421607

STORES
Debenhams
1-2 Robertson Street. Tel: (0424) 422601
Dengates

5 Cambridge Gardens. Tel: (0424) 426508
Marks & Spencer plc
30 Queens Road. Tel: (0424) 426707
Woolworths plc
1 Wellington Place. Tel: (0424) 421911

TAXIS
Ambassador Cars
3 Hughenden Road. Tel: (0424) 424557/721384
Anba Private Car Hire
278a Priory Road. Tel: (0424) 714262
C & C Cars
7 East Beech Street, Old Town. Tel: (0424) 431381/
444758/433390
G.R. Orr
21 Blacklands Drive. Tel: (0424) 435592
Taxi Rank
Havelock Road. Tel: (0424) 421581
Taybar Radio Taxis
278a Priory Road. Tel: (0424) 422386
Woodlands Taxis
35 Baldslow Road. Tel: (0424) 426860

THEATRES
George Street Hall
10 George Street. Tel: (0424) 427888
Stables Theatre
High Street. Tel: (0424) 423221
White Rock Theatre
White Rock. Tel: (0424) 722755/721210//434091

TOURIST OFFICES
**Hastings & St. Leonards Hotels & Tourism
Association**
Queensbury House, Havelock Road. Tel: (0424) 444005
Tourist Information Centre
4 Robertson Terrace. Tel: (0424) 722022
Tourist Information Centre (summer only)
The Fish Market, Old Town. Tel: (0424) 721201

❧ ❧ ❧ ❧ ❧ ❧ ❧

HEATHFIELD

A modern town, this was the site of the annual
Cuckoo Fair. On the 14th of every April, an old
lady was said to have released a cuckoo from a
basket, announcing the start of summer. To the
east of the town is Heathfield Park, site of the folly
known as Gibraltar Tower. Built in honour of Sir
George Elliot, Governor of Gibraltar, who success-
fully defended the colony against combined French
and Spanish attacks between 1779 and 1783.
Population: 6,207.

RESTAURANTS

Cades Country Kitchen
Cade Street. Tel: (043 52) 2209

The Chipmonk
6 Station Approach. Tel: (043 52) 2786

The Chippy
43 High Street. Tel: (043 52) 5282

Coffee Break
Heffle Corner, Station Approach. Tel: (043 52) 3381

Curry Inn
Hobby Day, Station Approach. Tel: (043 52) 4930/3227

Heathfield Tandoori
Burwash Road. Tel: (043 52) 3196

Master Chef
Elizabeth Catts Premises, Upper Station Road. Tel: (043 52) 2342

Super Star
78 High Street. Tel: (043 52) 4600

PUBLIC HOUSES

The Cross In Hand
 Tel: (043 52) 2053

The Crown
Burwash Road. Tel: (043 52) 2054

The Jack Cade
Cade Street. Tel: (043 52) 2209

The Prince of Wales
Station Road. Tel: (043 52) 2919

Star Inn
Church Street, Old Heathfield. Tel: (043 52) 3570

OTHER AMENITIES

CARAVAN PARK
Greenviews Caravan Park
Broad Oak. Tel: (043 52) 3531

FLORIST
Seasons
81 High Street. TN21 8JA Tel: (043 52) 2542

HEALTH CLUB
The Heathfield Health Club
1 Station Road. Tel: (043 52) 5787

RIDING SCHOOLS
Levade Systems
Little Willows, Hailsham Road. Tel: (043 52) 2200

C.C. Sansom
Sky Farm, Cade Street. Tel: (043 52) 2807

TAXIS
Avalon Cars
3 Yew Tree Close. Tel: (043 52) 3474

Heathfield Taxis

52 Leeves Close. Tel: (043 52) 2263

Thompsons Car Hire
Glendean, Station Approach. Tel: (043 52) 3491

❧ ❧ ❧ ❧ ❧ ❧ ❧

HELLINGLY

Hellingly reputedly has the only intact circular churchyard in the county, dating back to the 8th century, and the layout of much of the old village still follows that circular shape.
Population: 4,710.

PLACES OF INTEREST

Horselunges Manor
One of the most spectacular timber houses in the county.

RESTAURANT

Sussex Crest Restaurant
Golden Martlett , Station Road. Tel: (0323) 847909

PUBLIC HOUSE

The Golden Martlet
Station Road. Tel: (0323) 843728

OTHER AMENITY

GARDEN CENTRE
Nielsen Plants Ltd
Danecroft Nurseries , Station Road. Tel: (0323) 845211

HOSPITAL
Hellingly Hospital
Tel: (0323) 844391

❧ ❧ ❧ ❧ ❧ ❧ ❧

HERSTMONCEUX

Pronounced 'Herstmonsoo',the site of the only red brick castle in Sussex built in the 15th century, and not open to the public. It is supposedly haunted and has a history of eccentrics and murderous reprobates. Until recently the home of the Royal Observatory, now up for sale.
Population: 2,226.

PLACES OF INTEREST

Herstmonceux Castle
A castle on a domestic scale, extensively restored earlier this century. Until recently part of the Royal Observatory, whose headquarters are in Greenwich.

HOTELS

Cleavers Lyng Country Hotel
Church Road. Tel: (0323) 833131

HERSTMONCEUX CASTLE

The Horse Shoe Inn
Windmill Hill. Tel: (0323) 833265
White Friars Hotel & Restaurant
Tel: (0323) 832355
The Woolpack Hotel
Hailsham Road. Tel: (0323) 833270

GUEST HOUSE
Bazaar House
Gardener Street. Tel: (0323) 832575

RESTAURANTS
The Chestnut Tree Restaurant
High Street, Boreham Street. Tel: (0323) 833651
Eastern Promise
Gardner Street. Tel: (0323) 832533
Sundial Restaurant
Gardner Street. Tel: (0323) 832217

PUBLIC HOUSES
The Bulls Head Inn
Boreham Street. Tel: (0323) 832143
The Welcome Stranger

Chapel Row , Church Road. Tel: (0323) 832119
The White Horse Inn
Bodle Street. Tel: (0323) 833243

CAFÉ/TEA ROOMS
Samovar Restaurant
London House , Gardner Street. Tel: (0323) 832533

OTHER AMENITIES
CARAVAN PARK
Orchard View Caravan Park
Victoria Road, Windmill Hill. Tel: (0323) 832335

FISH FARM
Furnace Brook Trout Farm & Fishery
Trolliloes, Fishmarket Road. Tel: (0323) 830298

GARDEN CENTRES
Coopers Croft Nurseries
New Road. Tel: (0323) 832151
Lime Cross Nursery
Tel: (0323) 833229

TAXI
Autopoint
Windmill Hill Garage, Windmill Hill. Tel: (0323) 832430
Coach company
Months Open: Jan-Dec. Days Open: Mon-Fri. Hours Open:
9am-5pm. Proprietors: B P & J Ropemark.

🐾 🐾 🐾 🐾 🐾 🐾 🐾

HIGH HURSTWOOD
Two and a half miles north of Buxted. The church of The Holy Trinity is beautifully set in a dell. Best seen when the rhododendrons in the parsonage garden are in bloom.

OTHER AMENITY
HOSTEL
St. Bernadette Ltd.
High Hurstwood House, Chillies Lane. Tel: (082 581) 2139/2453

🐾 🐾 🐾 🐾 🐾 🐾 🐾

HOLLINGTON
Now a suburb of Hastings, with a medieval church of St Leonard.
Population: 4,664.

HOTEL
High Beach Hotel
Battle Road. Tel: (0424) 51383

PUBLIC HOUSES
The Rising Sun
173 Battle Road. Tel: (0424) 427030
The Royal Albert
293 Battle Road. Tel: (0424) 51066
Victoria Inn
Battle Road. Tel: (0424) 51755

🐾 🐾 🐾 🐾 🐾 🐾 🐾

HOOE
A mile north of the A 259 coast road, and to the west of Bexhill. William and his Normans would have passed through here on their way to Battle, when the area was a marshy inlet.
Population: 361.

PUBLIC HOUSES
The Lamb Inn
Tel: (042 43) 3828
The Red Lion
Tel: (0424) 892371

HORAM
Until the 1940s, maps showed this delightful village as Horeham Road. It has been established that this was a derivation of Whore's Home, and hence the change. Happily it is still a centre of pleasure, the makers of Merrydown cider having established here in 1947. The cider press is by the main road.
Population: 2,257.

PLACES OF INTEREST
Sussex Farm Museum
Tel: (04353) 2597
Months Open: Easter - October. Days Open: Everyday. Hours
Open: 10am - 5pm.

HOTEL
The Horam Hotel
High Street. Tel: (043 53) 2692

PUBLIC HOUSES
Gun Inn
Gun Hill. Tel: (0825) 872361
May Garland Inn
Tel: (043 53) 2249

CAFÉ/TEA ROOMS
Home Maid
High Street. Tel: (043 53) 2526

OTHER AMENITIES
CAR HIRE/SELF DRIVE
Trust Vehicle Services
Whatleys Garage, High Street. TN21 0EL Tel: (043 53) 2995

GARDEN CENTRE
Thorpe Gardens Ltd.
Little London Road. Tel: (043 53) 2455

RIDING SCHOOL
Horam Manor Riding Stables
Tel: (043 53) 2363

🐾 🐾 🐾 🐾 🐾 🐾 🐾

HOVE
Hove lies adjacent to Brighton, but the change in atmosphere as you move from one to the other is unmistakable. Hove is genteel and opulent, full of wide avenues, elegant squares and crescents, and parks. Beneath a bronzed statue of Queen Victoria on Grand Avenue, the hallowed Victorian values are inscribed in stone: Empire, Education, Science

THE BRITISH ENGINEERIUM

and Art, and Commerce. Hove is a testament to this philosophy. It is also home to Sussex County Cricket Club, which, with its proximity to the sea, is one of the most pleasant county grounds.
Population: 85,092.

PLACES OF INTEREST

British Engineerium
off Nevill Road.
Tel: (0273) 559583
A unique working steam museum, telling the history of hundreds of models and full size engines of steam power on land, sea, road and rail. Restoration projects in industrial archaeological material for national and private collections worldwide.
Months Open: All year. Days Open: Every day (Steaming days are Sundays and Bank Holidays). Hours Open: 10am - 5pm. Admission: £1.80. Children 75p. Access for the disabled.

Hove Museum & Art Gallery
19, New Church Road.
Tel: (0273) 779410
The museum boasts some fine displays of local history, including a Sussex room showing the home of a yeoman from the beginning of the 18th Century. 20th Century paintings and drawings. Pictures, furniture and decorative arts, dolls, toys, medals and coins. Special exhibitions of historic art and crafts.
Months Open: March - September. Days Open: Tuesday - Sunday. Hours Open: Tues - Fri 10am - 5pm; Sat 10am - 4.30pm; Sun 2 - 5pm. Admission: Free.

HOTELS

Adastral
8, Westbourne Villas. BN3 4GQ. Tel: (0273) 821541

The Albany Hotel
5, St Catherines Terrace. Tel: (0273) 773807

Alexandra Hotel
42, Brunswick Terrace. Tel: (0273) 202722

Bryandale Hotel
61, St Aubyns. Tel: (0273) 772152

Chatsworth Private Hotel
9, Salisbury Road. Tel: (0273) 737360

Cinderella Hotel
48, St Aubyns. Tel: (0273) 727827

The Claremont Hotel
13, Second Avenue. Tel: (0273) 735161

Conqueror Inn
16, Lower Market Street. Tel: (0273) 733513

Cornerways Hotel
18/20, Caburn Road. Tel: (0273) 731882

The Croft Hotel
24, Palmeria Avenue. Tel: (0273) 732860

The Cumberland Hotel
97, Lansdown Place. Tel: (0273) 732325

The Devonshire Hotel
38, St Aubyns. Tel: (0273) 733640

Downe House Hotel
93, Lansdowne Place. Tel: (0273) 737274

Dudley Hotel
Lansdowne Place. Tel: (0273) 736266

Edwards Hotel
11, Second Avenue. Tel: (0273) 771511

Hangleton Manor Inn
Hangleton Valley Drive. Tel: (0273) 413266

The Hotel Seafield
23, Seafield Road. Tel: (0273) 735912

Hovedean Hotel
15/17, The Drive. Tel: (0273) 733766

The Imperial Hotel
First Avenue. Tel: (0273) 731121

Inn off the Street
9, Waterloo Street. Tel: (0273) 720235

Langfords Hotel
12, Third Avenue. Tel: (0273) 738222

Langham Hotel
2 / 4, York Road. Tel: (0273) 731912

The Lawns Hotel
Kingsway. BN3 2GT. Tel: (0273) 736277

Macy's Private Hotel
61, Brunswick Place. Tel: (0273) 777562

Milton Hotel
81, St Aubyns. Tel: (0273) 738587

Peach house Hotel
7, Waterloo Street. Tel: (0273) 26056

Portland Hotel
Portland Road. Tel: (0273) 733164

The Sackville Hotel
189, Kingsway. Tel: (0273) 736292

eaholme Hotel
) - 11, Seafield Road. Tel: (0273) 731066

he Ship Hotel
love Street. Tel: (0273) 734936

t Catherines Lodge Hotel
ingsway. BN3 2RZ. Tel: (0273) 778181

he Terrace Hotel
3/29, Brunswick Terrace. Tel: (0273) 820080

Vhitehaven Hotel
4, Wilbury Road. Tel: (0273) 778355

GUEST HOUSES

runswick House
1, Brunswick Square. Tel: (0273) 26070

:ross Street Guest House
3, Cross Street. Tel: (0273) 770633

alkey Guest House
2, Portland Road. Tel: (0273) 778196

regenda Guest House
8, Davigdor Road. Tel: (0273) 739161

iriffon Guest house
9 Montefiore Road . Tel: (0273) 732760

ichfield Guest House
0, Waterloo street. Tel: (0273) 777740

he Only Alternative Left
9, St. Aubyns. Tel: (0273) 24739

amela Guest House
2, Portland Road. Tel: (0273) 776221

loberta Private Hotel
7, St. Aubyns. Tel: (0273) 733357

eafield Guest House
4, Seafield Road. Tel: (0273) 775954

RESTAURANTS

l Riaz Restaurant
44, Portland Road. Tel: (0273) 722332
Indian Cuisine. Specialities: Northwest Indian and Tandoori ishes. Hours Open: Lunch: 12 - 2.30pm. Dinner: 5.30 - 12 pm. ast Orders: 11.30pm. Open Sundays. Lunch: £ 5.95. House Vine: £ 5.95. Credit Cards: Ac. V. Seating Capacity: 40. Garden ables. N/S Areas. Veg. W/chair acc. B. P. W.

Ashoka Restaurant
5, Church Road. Tel: (0273) 734193

ali Brasserie Malaysian Indonesian Restaurant
irst Avenue, Kingsway. Tel: (0273) 23810

ilash Tandoori Restaurant
8, Church Road. Tel: (0273) 21636

istro Edward
7, Boundary Road. Tel: (0273) 411115

lossoms Coffee Shop
1, George Street. Tel: (0273) 776776

onaparte
0, Waterloo Street. Tel: (0273) 772922

he Caprice Restaurant
Third Avenue. Tel: (0273) 778737

Casbah Restaurant
5, Western Road. Tel: (0273) 731049

Chai Talay Restaurant
67, Church Road. Tel: (0273) 771170

Chez Bistro
38, Waterloo Street. Tel: (0273) 738412

Chez Maxime
10, Seaford Road. Tel: (0273) 423394

Crown of India Restaurant
99, Blatchington Road. Tel: (0273) 24404

The Curry Mahal Restaurant
171, Portland Road. Tel: (0273) 779125

Eaton Garden Restaurant
Eaton Gardens. Tel: (0273) 738921

Fairways Restaurant
182, Portland Road. BN32 5QN Tel: (0273) 734240

The Fig Leaf
37, Waterloo Street. Tel: (0273) 732383

Frascati Restaurant
8, Church Road. Tel: (0273) 24080

The Freemasons
39, Western Road. Tel: (0273) 732043

Georgies Bistro
85, George Street. Tel: (0273) 776063

Golden Tandoori Restaurant
7, Boundary Road. Tel: (0273) 413007

Goodwill
130, Portland Road. Tel: (0273) 739048

Halangers Bistro
14, Blatchington Road. Tel: (0273) 205009

Holland & Barrett Restaurant
122, Church Road. Tel: (0273) 729774

Hove Manor Restaurant
5, Hove Manor Parade. BN3 2DF Tel: (0273) 730850

Hove Rendezvous Chinese Restaurant
208, Church Road. Tel: (0273) 722475

Hove Tandoori
175, Church Road. Tel: (0273) 737188

The Inglenook Restaurant
68, Portland Road. Tel: (0273) 821335

Jaspers Restaurant
91, Church Road. Tel: (0273) 734705

Karims Tandoori
15, Blatchington Road. Tel: (0273) 739780
Indian Cuisine. Credit Cards: Ac. Am. D. V. Seating Capacity: 38. Veg. P. W.

Kashmir Indian Restaurant
71, Old Shoreham Road. Tel: (0273) 29264

Kestrels Rest
181, Portland Road. Tel: (0273) 739992

King Alfred Cafeteria
Kingsway. Tel: (0273) 737206

L'Epicure Restaurant Francais

48, Livingstone Road. Tel: (0273) 779954
Le Classique
37, Waterloo Street. BN3 1AY Tel: (0273) 734140
The Lido Restaurant
121, Western Road. Tel: (0273) 738352
The Mandarin Chinese Restaurant
36, Church Road. Tel: (0273) 734436
Mumtaj Mahal (Tandoori) Restaurant
4, Church Road. Tel: (0273) 731354
Nutmegs
70, Church Road. Tel: (0273) 771739
The Peking Restaurant
9, Western Road. Tel: (0273) 722090
Richards Restaurant
102, Western Road . Tel: (0273) 720058
Sackville Hotel Restaurant
189, Kingsway. BN3 4GV Tel: (0273) 736292
Secrets Restaurant
First Avenue. Tel: (0273) 731126
St Catherine's Lodge Hotel
Seafront, Kingway. Tel: (0273) 778181
The Stadium
253, Old Shoreham Road. Tel: (0273) 737981
The Swan Tandoori Restaurant
56, The Drive. Tel: (0273) 772210
Teaplanters Tiffin House
60, Western Road. Tel: (0273) 21343
Topolino's Restaurant
77, Church Road. Tel: (0273) 725726
Twizzle's
40, Western Road. Tel: (0273) 774341
Uncle Sams Hamburger Express
3, School Road. Tel: (0273) 776839
West End Restaurant
Western Lawns, Kingsway. Tel: (0273) 738436

PUBLIC HOUSES

The Albion Inn
110, Church Road.
Aldrington
90, Portland Road.
The Belfast Tavern
Belfast Street. Tel: (0273) 739495
Bow Street Runner
Brunswick Street. Tel: (0273) 27688
The Brunswick
3, Holland Road. Tel: (0273) 731676
The Cliftonville Hotel
100, Goldstone Villas. Tel: (0273) 733660
The Downsman
Hangleton Way. Tel: (0273) 777419
The Eclipse
Montgomery Street. Tel: (0273) 771624
Farm Tavern

Farm Road. Tel: (0273) 25905
Finch 's Bar
21, Western Road. Tel: (0273) 724194
The Freemasons Tavern
39, Western Road. Tel: (0273) 732043
The Golden Cross
Portland Road. Tel: (0273) 413372
The Grenadier Public House
200, Hangleton Road. Tel: (0273) 735901
Hove Place
37, First Avenue. Tel: (0273) 738266
Kendal Arms
Payne Avenue. Tel: (0273) 733860
The Mary Pack's
1, Hove Place. Tel: (0273) 770034
Brewery: Whitbread. Licensee: E.T. Wright. Opening Hours
10.30-3.00/5.30-11.00. Open all day Fri & Sat. Beer available
Flowers, Pompey, Strongs, Whitbread, Stella, Heineken
Murphys. Food Available: 12.00-2.30 & 6.30-9.30.
Maxim's Bar
3, Adelaide Mansions. Tel: (0273) 820822
The Maytree
376, Old Shoreham Road. Tel: (0273) 420178
Neptune Inn
Kingsway. Tel: (0273) 736390
Palmeira Public House
Cromwell Road. Tel: (0273) 720641
The Seagull Tavern
156, Old Shoreham Road. Tel: (0273) 735622
The Star Of Brunswick
32, Brunswick Street. Tel: (0273) 771355
Stirling Arms
Stirling Place. Tel: (0273) 733134
The Sussex Cricketer
Eaton Road. Tel: (0273) 734541
The Sussex Hotel
St. Catherine's Terrace. Tel: (0273) 774792
The Wick Inn
63, Western Road. Tel: (0273) 736436

CAFÉS & TEA ROOMS

The Cafe
318, Portland Road. Tel: (0273) 421928
Coffee Lounge
4, Victoria Terrace. Tel: (0273) 721028
Coffee Pot Cafe
101, Portland Road. Tel: (0273) 731970
The Cosy Cafe
98, Goldstone Villas. Tel: (0273) 720370
Cup 'O' Chino
109, Blatchington Road. Tel: (0273) 28840
Feedwell
325, Kingsway. Tel: (0273) 417705
Graham's Cafe

2, Brunswick Street West. Tel: (0273) 735250
The Headlight Cafe
83, Kingsway. Tel: (0273) 411113
Herbies Cafe
5, Waterloo Street. Tel: (0273) 729435
Jack's Diner
3, Montefiore Road. Tel: (0273) 739483
The Lagoon Cafe
Kingsway. Tel: (0273) 410197
Lucy's Larder
30, Portland Road. Tel: (0273) 412390
Ma's Pantry Cafe
5a, Victoria Terrace. Tel: (0273) 728896
Marrocco's
, Kings Esplanade. Tel: (0273) 735098
Micks Cafe
9, Goldstone Road. Tel: (0273) 738146
Palmeira Cafe
1, Western Road. Tel: (0273) 776607
The Railway Approach Tea Bar
Railway Approach, Goldstone Villas. Tel: (0273) 733574
Stadium Cafe
76b, Old Shoreham Road. Tel: (0273) 773202

OTHER AMENITIES

ART GALLERIES
Heritage Prints
7, Aymer Road. Tel: (0273) 720187
Viccari Art Gallery
21/23, Stirling Place. Tel: (0273) 733633

BUS & COACH SERVICES
Brighton & Hove Bus & Coach Company
43, Conway Street. BN3 3LT Tel: (0273) 206666

CAR HIRE
Andy's Chauffeur Drive
53, Glebe Villas. Tel: (0273) 411865
Cars For Brides
2, Wilbury Grove. Tel: (0273) 723090
Coopers Self Drive
58, Newtown Road. Tel: (0273) 206461
Grosvenor Chauffeur Services
61, Walsingham Road. Tel: (0273) 611958
Hannington's Limousine Hire
4 - 6, Montefiore Road. Tel: (0273) 732080
Kenning Car & Van Rental
Newtown Road. Tel: (0273) 821422
Lyons Chauffeur Services
23, St.Heliers Avenue. Tel: (0273) 735810
P. R. Car Hire
48, Brunswick Street. Tel: (0273) 738611
Personal Private Hire
7, Nevill Close. Tel: (0273) 502323

Strafford Rent-A-Car
Lancaster Court, Kingsway. Tel: (0273) 207373
Terry McCrae Car Hire
1, Victoria Terrace. Tel: (0273) 204717
Wadham Stringer
154, Old Shoreham Road. Tel: (0273) 26264/723771

CINEMA
Dorchester Cinema
27, Palmeira Avenue. Tel: (0273) 735124

GARDEN CENTRES
Adames of Hove
70/72, Portland Road. Tel: (0273) 731383
The Conservatory
The Drive. Tel: (0273) 731759
The Wheelbarrow
31, Montefiore Road . Tel: (0273) 737544

HEALTH CLUBS
The Body Shop
91, George Street. Tel: (0273) 771339
Brunswick Health Spa.
6, Brunswick Mews. Tel: (0273) 28535
Health Studio
93a, Boundary Road. Tel: (0273) 421900
Sunland Health Club
34a, Waterloo Street. Tel: (0273) 777409

HOSPITAL
Hove General Hospital
Sackville Road. Tel: (0273) 735244 / 737521

NIGHT CLUB
Cheminee Night Club
5, Western Road. Tel: (0273) 736019

RAILWAY STATION
Hove Station
Goldstone Villas. Tel: (0273) 732002

STORES
Army & Navy Stores
141, Churchill Road. Tel: (0273) 739222
Chiesmans
141, Church Road. Tel: (0273) 720851
Vokins
85, Blatchington Road. Tel: (0273) 26022
Woolworths
113/119, Blatchington Road. Tel: (0273) 736444

SWIMMING POOL
King Alfred Sports Centre
Kingsway. Tel: (0273) 734422

TAXIS

Blatchington Cabs
53, Blatchington Road. Tel: (0273) 737315
D.J.R. Meakin
2, Silverdale Road. Tel: (0273) 730475
Portland Cabs
10, Portland Road. Tel: (0273) 26939
Private Hire Cars
24, Rutland Gardens. Tel: (0273) 422415
Southern Streamline
162, Church Road. Tel: (0273) 775544/771835
R. A. Stevenson
38, Moyne Close. Tel: (0273) 776686
Streamline Taxis
86, Goldstone Villas. Tel: (0273) 736226/202020
Proprietor: Mr David Costa.

WATER SPORTS

Hove Lagoon Windsurfing School
Waterside, Kingsway. Tel: (0273) 430100

🐦 🐦 🐦 🐦 🐦 🐦 🐦

HURST GREEN

The countryside to the north of the village is remarkably beautiful, and although the village itself has been damaged by traffic and development, there are one or two fine Georgian buildings.
Population: 1,270.

HOTELS

Royal George Hotel
London Road. Tel: (058 086) 200
The Woolpack Inn
London Road. Tel: (058 086) 721

RESTAURANTS

The Little Chef
Horseshoe Motoring Centre. Tel: (058 086) 331
The Pleasant Place
83 London Road. Tel: (058 086) 321

PUBLIC HOUSES

Cross Keys Inn
London Road. Tel: (058 086) 332
The Old Bull Inn
40 London Road. Tel: (058 086) 257

🐦 🐦 🐦 🐦 🐦 🐦 🐦

ICKLESHAM

This ancient settlement, first recorded in 772 when it was granted to the Bishop of Selsey, is on the A 259 coast road between Hastings and Rye. It marks the eastern edge of the Hastings peninsular, th extreme of the Conqueror's beachhead. The churc of All Saints is a fascinating piece of early Norma architecture.
Population: 2,229.

HOTEL

PUBLIC HOUSES

Queens Head Inn
Parsonage Lane. Tel: (0424) 814552
Robin Hood Inn
Main Road. Tel: (0424) 814277

OTHER AMENITY

CAR HIRE/CHAUFFEUR DRIVEN
Chauffeur Services
16 Goldhurst Green. Tel: (0424) 814588

🐦 🐦 🐦 🐦 🐦 🐦 🐦

IDEN

Once owned by Nicholas de la Beche, who shared the rare distinction with two other knights of receiving a gift of £20, for helping to pull Edward I out of bed in time for mass, one Easter Monday.
Population: 520.

PUBLIC HOUSES

The Bell Inn
Tel: (079 78) 242
William The Conqueror
Tel: (079 78) 437

OTHER AMENITY

TAXI
Rother Cabs
11 Elmsmead Cottages. Tel: (079 78) 496

🐦 🐦 🐦 🐦 🐦 🐦 🐦

ISFIELD

A working agricultural village close to the spot where the old Roman road crossed the River Ouse. In the church near the river is the beautiful effigy to Sir John Shurley, his two wives, five daughters and four sons.
Population: 498.

HOTEL

The Laughing Fish Hotel
Tel: (082 575) 349

PUBLIC HOUSE
The Halfway House
Rose Hill. Tel: (082 575) 382

OTHER AMENITY
RAILWAY STATION
Lavender Line
sfield Railway Station. Tel: (082 575) 515

🐝 🐝 🐝 🐝 🐝 🐝 🐝

JARVIS BROOK

RESTAURANT
The Chip Inn
Beechview Parade, Walshes Road. Tel: (0892) 654514

OTHER AMENITY
TAXI
Skyline Taxis
Heatherview, Crowborough Hill. Tel: (0892) 652133

🐝 🐝 🐝 🐝 🐝 🐝 🐝

KINGSTON
What was a lovely village has been developed as almost a suburb of Lewes. The village pub, however, makes a good terminus for a downs walk from Woodingdean.
Population: 793.

PUBLIC HOUSE
The Juggs Arms
Little Orchard Street. Tel: (0273) 472523

OTHER AMENITY
GARDEN CENTRE
Sussex County Gardens
Newhaven Road. Tel: (0273) 473510

🐝 🐝 🐝 🐝 🐝 🐝 🐝

LAUGHTON
A scattered village west of Lewes on a flat plain, whose church has Pelham buckles on the tower.

PUBLIC HOUSE
The Roebuck Inn
Lewes Road. Tel: (032 183) 464

OTHER AMENITY
HOSPITAL
Laughton Lodge Hospital
Tel: (032 183) 451

LEWES BARBICAN

LEWES
The county town of East Sussex, Lewes has a long and important history stretching back to Saxon times. William the Conqueror established a castle here on a hill-top, which survived until 1620, when most of it was pulled down and the stone used for other buildings. It was in Lewes that Simon de Montfort led the barons against Henry III; and here lie the mortal remains of Gundrada, William the Conqueror's daughter, who founded the priory. Tom Paine was a customs man here when he wrote 'The Rights of Man'. Lewes is as charming a small town as you could wish for, set between two spurs of the downs, on the River Ouse. The High Street, lined with interesting Georgian buildings, rises steeply from the river. The Prince Regent was said to have driven a coach and horses down Keere Street, one of the almost vertical roads that runs off the High Street to the south. The prison and some office blocks do more to ruin the view from the downs than destroy the atmosphere once you are in the town. *Population: 78,233.*

PLACES OF INTEREST
Anne of Cleves House
A part of her dowry from Henry VIII. It is a well preserved picturesque timber-framed medieval building from the late c16.
Barbican House Museum
169, High Street.

LEWES CASTLE

Bull House

Near the West Gate. It was here that the great democrat Tom Paine lodged when he wrote 'that execrable book' The Age of Reason.

Castle

Founded by William de Warenne, one of the Conqueror's barons, circa 1100, and boasting one of the finest barbicans in Britain.

Lewes History Centre

Barbican House, High Street.

Tel: (0273) 474379

There is a large model of the historic Lewes, with an approximate 25 minute audio-visual programme of the towns historical evolution.

Months Open: March to October. Days Open: Every day Hours Open: Monday - Saturday 10am - 5.30pm; Sunday 11am - 5pm. Admission: 95p. Children 50p.

Museum of Local History

Tel: (0273) 474610

Collection of household equipment, furniture, pottery, a gallery of Lewes history. Set in a picturesque half-timbered house.

Months Open: February - November. Days Open: Tuesday - Sunday. Hours Open: Tuesday - Saturday 10am - 5.30pm: Sundays 2 - 5.30pm. Admission: £1.00. Children 55p.

Museum of Sussex Archaeology

Barbican House, High Street.

Tel: (0273) 474379

Collection of prehistoric, Romano-British, Saxon an medieval antiquities relating to Sussex.

Months Open: April - October. Days Open: Every day. Hou Open: Monday - Saturday, 10am- 5.30pm; Sundays 11am 5.30pm. Admission: £1.25. Children half price. Admission als includes admission to Lewes Castle.

Newick Park

Tel: (082 572) 3633

An Elizabethan ironmaster's house c 1580, this lovel country house is predominantly Georgian. The 240 acre of farm and parkland include ferns, trees, and an extensiv collection of camellias, azaleas and rhododendrons. Beau tiful spring flowers, many species over 100 years old.

Months Open: Garden only March - October. Days Ope Everyday. Hours Open: 10.30am - 6pm. Admission: £1.00 House open for functions and conferences. Not suitable fo wheelchairs.

Priory of St Pancras

The first Cluniac house in Britain. Established by Willian de Warenne c 1080, though this building is known onl from excavations.

HOTELS

The Black Horse Hotel

Western Road. Tel: (0273) 473653

The Crown Hotel

Market Street. Tel: (0273) 480670

BEDROOMS: B&B £ 25.00 - £ 32.00. 6 Double, (3 en suite, TV, 6 phone, 6 tea/coffee) B&B £ 17.00 - £ 20.00. 5 Twin, (1 e suite, 5 TV, 2 phone, 5 tea/coffee) B&B £ 17.00 - £ 20.00. Family, (1 TV, 1 phone, 1 tea/coffee) £ 12.00-£ 15.00 Cred Cards: Ac.

Shelleys Hotel

High Street. Tel: (0273) 472361

The Snowdrop Inn

119, South Street. Tel: (0273) 472144

The Tatler Hotel

83, High Street. Tel: (0273) 472510

The White Hart Hotel

High Street. Tel: (0273) 476694

GUEST HOUSE

Berkeley House Hotel

2, Albion Street. BN7 2ND. Tel: (0273) 476057

RESTAURANTS

Barbican Restaurant

77, High Street. Tel: (0273) 475996

Bull House Restaurant Francais

92, High Street. Tel: (0273) 473936

Downland Tea Rooms

205, High Street. Tel: (0273) 475817

Ghandi Indian Restaurant

20, Fisher Street. Tel: (0273) 477340

KEERE STREET DOWN WHICH THE PRINCE REGENT WAS SAID TO HAVE DRIVEN A COACH AND HORSES

Indian Cuisine. Specialities: Ghandi special dishes.

Kenwards Restaurant

151a, High Street. Tel: (0273) 472343

La Cucina

13, Station Street. Tel: (0273) 476707

La Scarpina

8, South Street. Tel: (0273) 478120

The Light of Bengal

32, Lansdown Road. Tel: (0273) 477016

The Lotus Inn

13, Fisher Street. Tel: (0273) 471935

Newmarket Tavern

Brighton Road. Tel: (0273) 478017

Panda Garden Chinese Restaurant
162, High Street. Tel: (0273) 473235

Pattissons Restaurant
199, High Street. Tel: (0273) 472727

Roots
146, High Street. Tel: (0273) 478328

Russell's Restaurant
11, Eastgate Street. Tel: (0273) 411435

Seasons Vegetarian Restaurant
12, Fisher Street. Tel: (0273) 479279

Thackery's
3, Mailing Street. Tel: (0273) 474634

Trumps Restaurant
19-20, Station Street. Tel: (0273) 473906

Modern English Cuisine. Specialities: Local produce - game, fish etc. Hours Open: Lunch: 12.30-2.00. Dinner: 7.00-10.00. Last Orders: 10.00pm. Closed Sundays. House Wine: £7.95. Credit Cards: Ac. V. Seating Capacity: 32. Veg. W/chair acc. P. Recommendations: ER. M*

Weighed In Restaurant
Bear Lane. Tel: (0273) 447737

PUBLIC HOUSES

The Elephant & Castle
White Hill. Tel: (0273) 473797

The Fruiterers Arms
1, Sun Street. Tel: (0273) 475509

The Kings Head
9, Southover. Tel: (0273) 474628

The Lamb Inn
10, Fisher Street. Tel: (0273) 480663

The Landsdown Arms
Landsdown Place. Tel: (0273) 472807

Pelham Arms
High Street. Tel: (0273) 476149

Prince Of Wales Inn
Malling Hill. Tel: (0273) 474119

The Rainbow Tavern
179 High Street. Tel: (0273) 472170

The Royal Oak
Station Road. Tel: (0273) 474803

The Swan Inn
Southover High Street. Tel: (0273) 480211

Tally Ho
Landport. Tel: (0273) 474759

The Volunteer Inn
Eastgate Street. Tel: (0273) 478557

CAFÉS & TEA ROOMS

Fillers
19, Market Street. Tel: (0273) 477042

The Garden Room
14, Station Street. Tel: (0273) 478636

The Hot Dog Cafe
1 - 3 , Neville Road. Tel: (0273) 473503

OTHER AMENITIES

ART GALLERIES

Craftwork
The Old Needlemakers, West Street. Tel: (0273) 475433

The Felix Gallery
2, Sun Street. Tel: (0273) 472668

The Lewes Gallery
90, High Street. Tel: (0273) 473367

Southey Fine Art
19 Cliffe Industrial Estate, South Street. Tel: (0273) 480612

BUS & COACH SERVICES

Lewes Buses & Coaches
28 Cliffe Industrial Estate, South Street. Tel: (0273) 479123

Southdown Motor Services
Walwers Lane. Tel: (0273) 480218

CAR HIRE

L. A. Beck
Cliff Bridge. Tel: (0273) 473709

Caffyns
Western Road. Tel: (0273) 473221

GARDEN CENTRE

Elphicks Of Lewes
18, The Cliffe. Tel: (0273) 472444

HOSPITAL

Victoria Hospital
Nevill Road. Tel: (0273) 474153

HOSTEL

Youth Hostels Association
Bank Cotts Telscombe. Tel: (0273) 37077

STORES

Woolworths Plc
53, Cliffe High Street. Tel: (0273) 473627

SWIMMING POOL

Pells Swimming Pool
North Street. Tel: (0273) 472334

TAXIS

Becks Taxis
Cliff Bridge. Tel: (0273) 473709

George & Graham Taxis
30, Meridian Road. Tel: (0273) 477015

J.K. Taxis

23, Meridian Road. Tel: (0273) 473692
S & G Taxis
5 Riverside Estate, North Street. Tel: (0273) 472619

TOURIST INFORMATION OFFICE
Tourist Information Centre
32, High Street. Tel: (0273) 471600

WINE BAR
Mike's Wine Bar
197, High Street. Tel: (0273) 477879

🐦 🐦 🐦 🐦 🐦 🐦 🐦

LITLINGTON

A very beautiful village, which gives an excellent view of a (not very ancient) White Horse cut into the chalk of the downs opposite. This, and its undoubted charm, have helped to place it on the tourists' map.
Population: 109.

PUBLIC HOUSE
The Plough & Harrow
Tel: (0323) 870632

OTHER AMENITY
GARDEN CENTRE
Litlington Nurseries
Tel: (0323) 870222

🐦 🐦 🐦 🐦 🐦 🐦 🐦

LITTLE COMMON

On the A 259 just west of Bexhill. Now little more than a suburb.

PUBLIC HOUSES
The Village Mews Inn
Village Mews. Tel: (042 43) 3001
Wheatsheaf Inn
Tel: (042 43) 2004

🐦 🐦 🐦 🐦 🐦 🐦 🐦

LITTLE HORSTED

Between Lewes and Uckfield on the A22. The church of St Michael has a 'green man' in one of the carved spandrels of the doorway.
Population: 188.

HOTEL
Horsted Place
Tel: (082 575) 581

LOWER DICKER

A tiny village on the A 22, a mile west of Hailsham. Dickerware, a black pottery, comes from this area.

HOTEL
Boship Farm Hotel
Tel: (0323) 844826

RESTAURANTS
Happy Eater Restaurant
A22, London Road. Tel: (0825) 872020
The Little Chef
Tel: (0323) 843775

PUBLIC HOUSES
The Kings Head Hotel
Tel: (0323) 843712
The White Hart Inn
Tel: (0323) 840121
British Queen
The Triangle. Tel: (032 12) 4166

CAFÉ/TEA ROOMS
The Willow Cafe
Tel: (0323) 844594

OTHER AMENITY
GARDEN CENTRE
Victoria Nursery
A22. Tel: (0323) 845701 / 844834

TAXI
Timberdown Taxis
Tel: (0323) 844685

🐦 🐦 🐦 🐦 🐦 🐦 🐦

MARESFIELD

At the southern tip of Ashdown Forest. In the heyday of the Sussex iron industry, Maresfield once boasted three mills. Now it is a sprawling town, straddling the A 22.
Population: 3,457.

RESTAURANT
Budletts Restaurant
Budletts House, Budletts Common. Tel: (0825) 61325

PUBLIC HOUSE
The Chequers
High Street. Tel: (0825) 3843

OTHER AMENITIES

MAYFIELD'S MAIN STREET

CAR HIRE/SELF DRIVE
Maresfield Garage
London Road. Tel: (0825) 61655

GARDEN CENTRE
Doma Farm Nursery
Lampool Corner. TN22 3DR Tel: (082 571) 2884

TAXI
E.F. Motors
Furnace Bank House. Tel: (0825) 2000

🐦 🐦 🐦 🐦 🐦 🐦 🐦

MARK CROSS
In the wooded hills south of Tunbridge Wells, a genuine crossroads.

PUBLIC HOUSE
Mark Cross Inn
Tel: (089 285) 2423

OTHER AMENITY

GARDEN CENTRE
Sussex Country Gardens Ltd.
Eastbourne Road (A267). Tel: (089 285) 2828

🐦 🐦 🐦 🐦 🐦 🐦 🐦

MAYFIELD
The name is derived from Maid's Field, which may well refer to inhabitants of the Roman Catholic convent school built around the remains of Mayfield Palace, once the residence of medieval Archbishops of Canterbury. Mayfield was once a centre of Wealden ironworks, and prospered in the railway age. Now without a station, the town maintains an air of opulence, and there are some fine timber buildings in the main street.
Population: 3,242.

HOTEL
The Middle House Hotel
High Street. Tel: (0435) 872146

RESTAURANT

The Old Brewhouse Restaurant
High Street. Tel: (0435) 872342

PUBLIC HOUSES

The Carpenters Arms
Fletching Street. Tel: (0435) 873294
The Railway Inn
Stone Cross Road. Tel: (0435) 872529
Rose & Crown
Tel: (0435) 872200

CAFÉ/TEA ROOMS

April Cottage
West Street. Tel: (0435) 872160

OTHER AMENITIES

CAR HIRE/CHAUFFEUR DRIVEN
Mayfield Private Hire
8 Alexandra Road. Tel: (0435) 872332

RIDING SCHOOLS
Coggins Mill Riding & Livery Stables
Coggins Mill Farm. Tel: (0435) 873289
Knowle Livery & Training Yard
Newick Lane. Tel: (0435) 872387

THEATRE
Friends of Music in Mayfield
c/o Libra Bookshop, West Street. Tel: (0435) 873382

🐾 🐾 🐾 🐾 🐾 🐾 🐾

MAYNARDS GREEN

PUBLIC HOUSE

Runt In Tun
Tel: (043 52) 4284

OTHER AMENITY

GARDEN CENTRE
Funnells Farm Nurseries
Tel: (043 52) 2367

🐾 🐾 🐾 🐾 🐾 🐾 🐾

NETHERFIELD

A tiny village two miles north-west of Battle with a Victorian church.

RESTAURANT

Netherfield Place
Netherfield Place. Tel: (042 46) 4455

PUBLIC HOUSE

White Hart Inn & Restaurant
Tel: (042 482) 382

OTHER AMENITIES

TAXIS
I.R. Brown
50 Darvel Down. Tel: (042 482) 388
Hawk Cars
43 Darvel Down. Tel: (042 482) 434

🐾 🐾 🐾 🐾 🐾 🐾 🐾

NEWHAVEN

It is said that Louis Phillipe left the French throne and stayed here as plain Mr Smith. Nowadays most people visit Newhaven in transit to or from the Continent, and most of the energies of the townspeople are dedicated to servicing that requirement, and to producing Parker pens.
Population: 9,834.

PLACES OF INTEREST

Newhaven Museum
Contains an excellent collection of old photographs of Newhaven and the surrounding district.
Months Open: Easter - October. Days Open: Saturday, Sunday. Hours Open: 2.30 - 6pm . Bank Holidays: Open.

HOTELS

The Bridge Inn
High Street. Tel: (0273) 514059
The Sheffield Arms
Fort Road. Tel: (0273) 513340
The Ship Hotel
High Street. Tel: (0273) 514115

GUEST HOUSES

Always Guest House
72, Brighton Road. Tel: (0273) 717229
Old Volunteer Guest House
1, South Road. Tel: (0273) 515204
John & Evelyn Sewell
51, South Road. Tel: (0273) 514016

RESTAURANTS

Benbows Cafe
12, Bridge Street. Tel: (0273) 516334
Buttimers Seafood Restaurant
16/18, Chapel Street. Tel: (0273) 514632
The Cup and Saucer
17, Chapel Street. Tel: (0273) 514568
Ruchita Tandoori Restaurant
4a, Bridge Street. Tel: (0273) 514296/513308

Sun Do Restaurant
47, High Street. Tel: (0273) 514397

PUBLIC HOUSES

The Crown Inn
Bridge Street. Tel: (0273) 515333
The Engineer Inn
Railway Road. Tel: (0273) 514460
The Hope Inn
West Pier. Tel: (0273) 515389
The Jolly Boatman
135, Lewes Road. Tel: (0273) 514457
The Newfield Public House
Brighton Road. Tel: (0273) 513841
Newhaven Transit Tavern
Transit Road. Tel: (0273) 514338
The Prince Of Wales
49, South Road. Tel: (0273) 513364
The White Hart Hotel
High Street. Tel: (0273) 515218

CAFÉS & TEA ROOMS

The Buffet
Car Ferry Terminal, Railway Approach.
Tel: (0273) 513536
Coral Cabin Cafe
Coral Marine, Ford Road. Tel: (0273) 516143
Ferryside Coffee
38, Clifton Road. Tel: (0273) 514578
Mitchells Cafe
2 Coronation House, High Street. Tel: (0273) 515913
Riverside Snack Bar
West Quay. Tel: (0273) 515331
West Beach Kiosk
West Pier. Tel: (0273) 513514

OTHER AMENITIES

CAR HIRE
Dove Garage
Station Approach. Tel: (0273) 515303
Quarry Car Hire
Unit L, Quarry Road. Tel: (0273) 512905

CARAVAN PARK
Downland Caravan Site
Court Farm Road. Tel: (0273) 514351

HOSPITAL
Newhaven Downs Hospital
Church Hill. Tel: (0273) 513441

LEISURE CENTRES
Borowski Ski Centre
New Road . Tel: (0273) 515402

C J's Gym
3, Meeching Road. Tel: (0273) 512604

NIGHT CLUB
Cloud Nine Club
Rex Suite, High Street. Tel: (0273) 514140

RAILWAY STATION
Newhaven Town Station
Railway Approach. Tel: (0273) 514647

STORE
Woolworths Plc
14, High Street. Tel: (0273) 514499

SWIMMING POOL
Seahaven Swimming Pool
Southway. Tel: (0273) 512498

TAXIS
Allens Taxis
43, Marshall Lane. Tel: (0273) 513042
Bills Taxi
66, Wellington Road. Tel: (0273) 512625
Horace
7c, Chapel Street. Tel: (0273) 514764
Pauls Taxis
Portacabin, Railway Road, The Drove. Tel: (0273) 516846

❦ ❦ ❦ ❦ ❦ ❦ ❦

NEWICK

A settlement that has developed into an oval shape, with a delightful village green on which stands a long handled pump. St Mary's church has a Norman nave, and was restored by the Victorians.
Population: 2,419.

RESTAURANT
Newick Village Tandoori
7/9 Church Road. Tel: (082 572) 3628/3738

PUBLIC HOUSES
Bricklayers Arms
86 Allington Road. Tel: (082 572) 2976
Brewery: Phoenix. Licensee: Mr Nigel Gibson. OPEN ALL DAY. Opening Hours: 11am-11pm. Food Available: All day (including afternoon teas). Garden. Car Park .Traditional games: Darts and shove halfpenny.
The Bull Inn
The Green. Tel: (082 572) 2055
The Royal Oak
Church Road. Tel: (082 572) 2506

NEWICK PARK

A tiny collection of houses a mile and a half south of Newick itself.

OTHER AMENITY

GARDEN CENTRE
Sifelle Nursery
The Walled Garden. Tel: (082 572) 3073

🐦 🐦 🐦 🐦 🐦 🐦 🐦

NINFIELD

A village situated on a ridge. The little church of St Mary has a lovely working clock mechanism inside a blue frame. Outside are the village stocks, made in the Sussex fashion entirely from cast iron.
Population: 1,288.

HOTEL

The United Friends
The Green. Tel: (0424) 892462

PUBLIC HOUSE

Kings Arms
Bexhill Road. Tel: (0424) 892385/892263

OTHER AMENITIES

RIDING SCHOOL
C.A. Barclay
Moor Hall Stables, Moor Hall Hotel. Tel: (0424) 892908

TAXI
Ninfield Car Hire
38 Coombe Shaw. Tel: (0424) 892722

🐦 🐦 🐦 🐦 🐦 🐦 🐦

NORMAN'S BAY

This is where the Conqueror is thought to have landed in 1066. If he could return now he might be somewhat surprised by the shanty town that has grown around such a historic spot.

PUBLIC HOUSE

The Star Inn
Tel: (0323) 762648

OTHER AMENITY

TAXI
Terry's Taxis
The Old Mission. Tel: (0323) 761786

CARAVAN PARK
Normans Bay Caravan Parks. Tel: (0323) 761842

🐦 🐦 🐦 🐦 🐦 🐦 🐦

NORTHIAM

A delightful village with 18th century white weatherboard houses surrounding the village green. In 1573 Queen Elizabeth I dined under the great oak still standing on the green, when she was visiting Kent and Sussex. She left her green shoes behind and they are still displayed at Brickwall, a large Jacobean house now a boys school, when it is open to the public. Great Dixter is a 15th century house restored by Lutyens. The bridge over the Rother to the north of the village leads into Kent.
Population: 1,657.

PLACES OF INTEREST

Brickwall House
Tel: (0797) 252494
Home of the Frewen family since 1666. 17th century Plaster Ceilings. Family portraits spanning 400 years of history. Chess garden and arboretum.
Months Open: April - September. Days Open: Saturdays and Bank Holidays. Hours Open: 2 - 5pm. Admission: £1.00. Open at other times by prior arrangement with the curator. Tel: 0797 223329
Great Dixter
Tel: (0797) 253160
15th century half-timbered manor house in designed gardens.
Months Open: March - October. Days Open: Tuesday - Fridays, weekends in October.

HOTELS

Hayes Arms Hotel
Village Green. Tel: (0797) 253142
The Rother Valley Inn
Station Road. Tel: (0797) 252116

RESTAURANT

The Fish Bar
Main Street. Tel: (0797) 253157

PUBLIC HOUSE

Crown & Thistle
Tel: (0797) 253224

CAFÉ/TEA ROOMS

Mary Mason's Teahouse
Yew Tree Farm House, Beckley Road. Tel: (0797) 253154

OTHER AMENITIES

CAR HIRE/CHAUFFEUR DRIVEN
W. Wilson
Green Leigh, Station Road. Tel: (0797) 252136

GARDEN CENTRE
Just Roses
Beales Lane. Tel: (0797) 252355

🐦 🐦 🐦 🐦 🐦 🐦 🐦

NUTLEY

On the western edge of Ashdown Forest, Edward II had a hunting lodge here. One mile to the north is a windmill with its four sails intact.

RESTAURANTS
Forge Restaurant
High Street. Tel: (082 571) 3287
The Little Chef
Shelley Arms, High Street. Tel: (082 571) 2832
Fast food Cuisine. Specialities: Breakfasts. Last Orders: 10pm. Closed Christmas Day. Open Sundays. Credit Cards: Ac. Am. V. Seating Capacity: 56. Veg. W/chair. P.

PUBLIC HOUSES
The Shelley Arms
High Street. Tel: (082 571) 3121
William IV Inn
Tel: (082 571) 2671

OTHER AMENITY
RIDING SCHOOL
Misbourne Pony Trekking Centre
Misbourne Farm. Tel: (082 571) 2516

🐦 🐦 🐦 🐦 🐦 🐦 🐦

OFFHAM

Just north of Lewes, in the valley of the river Ouse. It was on Offham Hill that the Battle of Lewes took place in 1264 (see Fletching) and the remains of many bodies have been found in the nearby chalkpits.

PUBLIC HOUSES
The Blacksmiths Arms
Tel: (0273) 472971
The Chalk Pit Inn
Offham Road. Tel: (0273) 471124

CAFÉ/TEA ROOMS
Old Post House
Tel: (0273) 477358

🐦 🐦 🐦 🐦 🐦 🐦 🐦

ORE

A suburb on the eastern edge of Hastings. There

are ruins of the medieval church close to the later St Helen's.
Population: 5,232.

RESTAURANTS
Ellies Village Bistro
504 Old London Road. Tel: (0424) 425525
Kentucky Fried Chicken
472 Old London Road. Tel: (0424) 420062

PUBLIC HOUSES
Hare & Hounds Hotel
Old London Road. Tel: (0424) 422349
Old King John
Middle Road. Tel: (0424) 443310

OTHER AMENITIES
CARAVAN PARKS
Coghurst Hall Caravan Site
Ivy House Lane. Tel: (0424) 751185/751451
Spindlewood Country Caravan Park
Bricklands Farm, Rock Lane. TN35 4JN
Tel: (0424) 720825

HOSPITAL
St. Helens Hospital
Frederick Road. Tel: (0424) 720444

🐦 🐦 🐦 🐦 🐦 🐦 🐦

PATCHAM

The northern extent of Brighton, an old downland village with a Norman church.

PLACES OF INTEREST
Monument to the Hindus
As you enter Brighton on the A23, there is an eastern temple of Sicilian marble built in memory of the Sikhs and Hindus. They survived the battle fields of France during WW I only to die in Brighton. Their bodies were cremated here on a funeral pyre set on two stones that are still visible.

HOTEL
The Black Lion Hotel
London Road. Tel: (0273) 555522

PUBLIC HOUSE
Ladies Mile
2, Mackie Avenue. Tel: (0273) 554647

🐦 🐦 🐦 🐦 🐦 🐦 🐦

PEACEHAVEN

Peacehaven is where the Greenwich meridian

crosses the English coast. It was originally proposed to be called New Anzac-on-Sea, in honour of those who died at Galipolli. A financial scandal surrounded the selling of the building plots after the Second World War. The downs behind the village are as unchanged and enchanting as anywhere.

Population: 10,240.

PLACES OF INTEREST

CO-OP Shop
The Greenwich meridian runs through this store and on to bisect the world.

HOTELS

The Brighton Motel
1, South Coast Road. Tel: (0273) 583736
The Retreat
205, South Coast Road. Tel: (0273) 581743

GUEST HOUSE

Meridian Lodge Hotel
69, South Coast Road. Tel: (0273) 581764

RESTAURANTS

Olivers Restaurant
20, Steyning Avenue. Tel: (0273) 582291
Wimpy Restaurant
381 South Coast Road, Telscombe Cliff. Tel: (0273) 582256

PUBLIC HOUSES

Dewdrop Inn
19, Steyning Avenue. Tel: (0273) 582242
The McKellar
104, Roderick Avenue. Tel: (0273) 585695
The Sussex Coaster
80, South Coast Road. Tel: (0273) 582145

CAFÉS & TEA ROOMS

Long John's Coffee Bar
8 Meridian Centre, Roderick Avenue. Tel: (0273) 584127
Pantry
177, South Coast Road. Tel: (0273) 582354

OTHER AMENITIES

ART GALLERY
Peacehaven Framing Services
21a, Edith Avenue. Tel: (0273) 584030

CAR HIRE
Fenners Garage
79, South Coast Road. Tel: (0273) 587246
Peacehaven Hire
227, South Coast Road. Tel: (0273) 585212

CARAVAN PARKS

Rushey Hill Caravan Park
The Highway. Tel: (0273) 582344
Tudor Rose Park
South Coast Road. Tel: (0273) 582314

GARDEN CENTRES

Fixit Garden Supercentre
Tel: (0273) 587111
Poplett Of Peacehaven
174, South Coast Road. Tel: (0273) 583133

LEISURE CENTRE

Meridian Leisure Centre
Greenwich Way. Tel: (0273) 587803
Local Government Leisure Centre
Months Open: Jan-Dec. Days Open: Mon-Sun. Hours Open: Mon-Fri 10am-10pm Sat 9am-7pm Sun 10am-8pm. Open all Bank Holidays. Bowls Mon&Tues. Aerobics Mon&Wed. Mothers and toddlers Wed & Fri. Solarium (two sunbeds). Creche. Conditioning gym and sports hall. Manager: Mr Steve Blake.

TAXIS

Dave's Taxis
179, Roderick Avenue. Tel: (0273) 587119
R.B. Evans
14 Jason Close, Arundel Park. Tel: (0273) 583500
Meridian Centre Taxis
The Kiosk , Meridian Centre. Tel: (0273) 581072
Peacehaven Taxis & Hire Cars
36, Friars Avenue. Tel: (0273) 584356
South Coast Streamline Taxis
117, Roderick Avenue. Tel: (0273) 583400

🐎 🐎 🐎 🐎 🐎 🐎 🐎

PEASMARSH

Three rivers, the Rother, the Tillingham and the Brede drain the land to the north of Rye, and Peasmarsh sits slightly above the flood plain. The church of St Peter and St Paul, down a lane to the south of the village, has Norman elements.

Population: 940.

HOTEL

Flackley Ash Hotel & Restaurant
Tel: (079 721) 651/381/355

PUBLIC HOUSES

The Cock Inn
Main Street. Tel: (079 721) 281
Horse & Cart Inn

School Lane. Tel: (079 721) 220

OTHER AMENITY
FISH FARM
W. Ashdown & Son Ltd.
Main Street. Tel: (079 721) 241

🐦 🐦 🐦 🐦 🐦 🐦 🐦

PETT
The village is inland, looking down on Pett Level. This whole area is a coastal weak spot and attractive to would-be invaders. In fact the Germans planned to attack just east of Rye. The Victorian church with its peculiar octagonal tower and spire is given an unwholesome air by the plethora of ugly gargoyles.
Population: 653.

PUBLIC HOUSES
Royal Oak Inn
Pett Road. Tel: (0424) 812515
The Two Sawyers
Pett Road. Tel: (0424) 812255

OTHER AMENITIES
CARAVAN PARKS
Caravan Club Ltd.
Fairlight Wood Caravan Site. Tel: (0424) 812333
Carters Farm Holiday Caravan Park
Elm Lane. Tel: (0424) 813206

🐦 🐦 🐦 🐦 🐦 🐦 🐦

PETT LEVEL
An eccentric collection on the coast of caravans, bungalows and sea defences. Someone has even made a home from a converted gasometer! The large ponds are home to many wild fowl. At low tide the remains of a submerged prehistoric forest can be seen.

PUBLIC HOUSE
The Smuggler
Tel: (0424) 813491

OTHER AMENITY
TAXI
Alpha Taxis
Elm Cottage. Tel: (0424) 812243

🐦 🐦 🐦 🐦 🐦 🐦 🐦

PEVENSEY
The castle was originally raised by the Romans, some say Caesar himself stayed here. The Normans built on the Roman remains. Thomas À' Becket learned chivalry here, Simon de Montfort besieged it and John of Gaunt owned it.
Population: 2,668.

PLACES OF INTEREST
Pevensey Castle
Tel: (0323) 762604
An interesting monument to our only conquerors. The Norman castle stands on the ancient Roman walls. It is undoubtedly the best Roman site in the county.

HOTELS
The Priory Court Inn
Pevensey Castle. Tel: (0323) 763150
The Royal Oak and Castle
High Street. Tel: (0323) 762371

PUBLIC HOUSE
The Smugglers Inn
High Street. Tel: (0323) 762112

OTHER AMENITY
RAILWAY STATION
Pevensey & Westham Station
Eastbourne Road. Tel: (0323) 762250

🐦 🐦 🐦 🐦 🐦 🐦 🐦

PEVENSEY BAY
A straggle of bungalows cutting off Pevensey from the sea. The coastline in this area has undergone many changes over the years, with many towns, like Pevensey, two or three miles further inland than they were. Conversely there is evidence of much coastal erosion.

HOTEL
The Bay Hotel
2 - 4 , Eastbourne Road. Tel: (0323) 762014

GUEST HOUSE
Napier Guest House
The Promenade. Tel: (0323) 752002

RESTAURANTS
The Barnhill Restaurant
4, North Road. Tel: (0323) 761346
The Pepper Pot Restaurant
43, Eastbourne Road. Tel: (0323) 761914

PEVENSEY CASTLE STANDS ON ANCIENT ROMAN WALLS

PUBLIC HOUSES

The Beach Tavern
Tel: (0323) 761372
The Castle Inn
Eastbourne Road. Tel: (0323) 764970
The Moorings

Seaville Drive. Tel: (0323) 761126
Stable Sports Bar
Tel: (0323) 37867

CAFÉ/TEA ROOMS

The Sandwich Inn

Saxon Court, Eastbourne Road. Tel: (0323) 762610

OTHER AMENITIES

CAR HIRE
Cabby Valmida
Valprinceps Road. Tel: (0323) 762497

CARAVAN PARKS
Bay View Caravans
Old Martello Road. Tel: (0323) 768688
Martello Beach Caravan Park
Eastbourne Road. Tel: (0323) 761424
Summerdown Holiday Bungalows Ltd.
Tel: (0323) 761654

TAXI
Bay Cars
Eastbourne Road. Tel: (0323) 761270

🐾 🐾 🐾 🐾 🐾 🐾 🐾

PIDDINGHOE

A village north of Newhaven near the mouth of the River Ouse, with smuggling and fishing connections. In the days of the French raids on the coast, the view from the church tower served as an early warning system.
Population: 248.

PUBLIC HOUSE
The Royal Oak
Tel: (0273) 513610

🐾 🐾 🐾 🐾 🐾 🐾 🐾

PILTDOWN

This was where, in 1912, Charles Dawson claimed to have discovered the skull which, known as 'Piltdown Man', fooled the scientific establishment until 1953. It turned out to be the jaw bone of an orang-outang and a doctored human skull, but appealed to the public desire to discover the missing link.

RESTAURANT
The Little Chef
Piltdown Service Station. Tel: (082 572) 3922

PUBLIC HOUSE
The Piltdown Man
Tel: (082 572) 3349

🐾 🐾 🐾 🐾 🐾 🐾 🐾

PLAYDEN

On the hill down into Rye from Peasmarsh, the noticeably unrestored 13th century church, St Michael, has a particularly tall spire, with fine views of Rye below.
Population: 295.

HOTELS
Playden Oasts
Peasmarsh Road. Tel: (0797) 223502
BEDROOMS: 6 Double, (6 en suite, 6 TV, 6 phone, 6 tea/coffee) B&B £ 20.00 - £ 31.00. 2 Twin, (2 en suite, 2 TV, 2 phone, 2 tea/ coffee) B&B £ 20.00 - £ 31.00. RESTAURANT: English Cuisine. Lunch: £5.00. House Wine: £5.95. À La Carte: £13.00. Credit Cards: Ac. Am. D. V.
Rumpels Inn & Motel
Peasmarsh Road. Tel: (079 721) 494

PUBLIC HOUSES
Hare & Hounds
Peasmarsh Road. Tel: (079 721) 483
Peace & Plenty Inn
Peasmarsh Road. Tel: (079 78) 342

OTHER AMENITY
HOSPITAL
Rye, Winchelsea & District Memorial Hospital
Tel: (0797) 222109/223810

🐾 🐾 🐾 🐾 🐾 🐾 🐾

PLUMPTON

Near the site of a famous Bronze Age settlement, Plumpton is on the spring-line north of the downs. It is now known for its racecourse, and for the Agricultural college near the Norman church of St Michael, which stands alone in the field in the lee of the downs. The home of John Dudeney, a shepherd who taught himself Hebrew, French, Mathematics, Geometry and, with the aid of a homemade telescope, Astronomy. He later became a schoolmaster and was instrumental in founding Lewes Mechanics Institute.
Population: 1,305.

PLACES OF INTEREST
Plumpton Place
Originally built in the late 16th and early 17th centuries and extensively restored by Lutyens in the 1920s. A magnificent moated house lying in the shelter of the downs, latterly the home of Jimmy Page of 'Led Zeppelin'. Not open to the public.

HOTEL

The Plough Inn
North Plumpton. Tel: (0273) 890311

PUBLIC HOUSE

The Half Moon
Ditchling Road. Tel: (0273) 890253

🐴 🐴 🐴 🐴 🐴 🐴 🐴

PLUMPTON GREEN

HOTEL

The Sun Hotel
Station Road. Tel: (0273) 890571

PUBLIC HOUSES

The Fir & Feather
Station Road. Tel: (0273) 890583
The Fountain
Station Road. Tel: (0273) 890294

🐴 🐴 🐴 🐴 🐴 🐴 🐴

POLEGATE

One of the villages to the north of Eastbourne that
has been absorbed by urbanisation.
Population: 6,794.

PLACES OF INTEREST

Filching Manor
Tel: (032 12) 7838/7124
The Manor is set in 28 acres of downland and formal
gardens. A medieval construction, it includes the unique
minstrels' gallery. The oak panelling between the hall and
the drawing room represents the earliest type known. An
underground passage runs from the cellars. There is a
collection of classic motor cars.
Months Open: March - October. Days Open: Thursday -
Sunday. Hours Open: 10.30am - 4.30pm (other times by
appointment only). Admission: £2.00. Children half price. Suit-
able for disabled. Light refreshments.
Windmill
Built in 1817, this tower mill has all four of its sails still
surviving.

RESTAURANTS

Country Kitchen Restaurant & Cafe
Nightinghale Hill. Tel: (032 12) 2621
Dean Tandoori
5, Grand Parade. Tel: (032 12) 5248
Gibby's Licensed Restaurant
Jevington Road. Tel: (032 12) 2484
The Horse and Groom

1, High Street. Tel: (032 12) 3037
The Hungry Monk
Jevington. Tel: (032 12) 2178
The Mill Restaurant
Unit 6, The Centre. Tel: (032 12) 3356

PUBLIC HOUSES

Dinkum
54, High Street. Tel: (032 12) 2029
The Junction Tavern
99, Station Road. Tel: (032 12) 2010
The Thoroughbred
6, Grand Parade. Tel: (032 12) 4023

OTHER AMENITIES

RAILWAY STATION
Polegate Station
Station Road. Tel: (032 12) 3034

TAXIS
A-2-B Taxis
53, Station Road. Tel: (032 12) 7191
Abal Car Hire
3, Hazel Grove. Tel: (032 12) 2264
Fleetline Radio Cars
36, High Street. Tel: (032 12) 6697
Polegate & Westham Station Taxis
97, Station Road. Tel: (032 12) 4253/7777

🐴 🐴 🐴 🐴 🐴 🐴 🐴

PORTSLADE

Now simply an extension of the Brighton/Hove
conurbation.
Population: 17,955.

PUBLIC HOUSES

The Alexandra Inn
Wellington Road. Tel: (0273) 413019
The Battle Of Trafalgar
77, Trafalgar Road. Tel: (0273) 416714
The Blue Anchor
Station Road. Tel: (0273) 413046
The Cricketers Arms
49, Church Road. Tel: (0273) 417957
The Fishersgate Inn
Gardener Road. Tel: (0273) 411149
The Halfway House
1, Wellington Road. Tel: (0273) 413080
The Mile Inn
Mill Lane. Tel: (0273) 420187
Railway Hotel
Station Road. Tel: (0273) 419582
St. George Inn

High Street. Tel: (0273) 419019
Stags Head Public House
37, High Street. Tel: (0273) 417337
The Sussex Arms
87, Fishersgate Terrace. Tel: (0273) 413269

CAFÉS & TEA ROOMS
C.J.'s Cafe
80, Station Road. Tel: (0273) 430642
Little Chalet Cafe
111, Victoria Road. Tel: (0273) 422320

OTHER AMENITIES
BUS & COACH SERVICES
Bus Parts
Victoria Road. Tel: (0273) 412456

HOSTEL
Young Mens Christian Association
George Williams House, 50 Highlands Road.
Tel: (0273) 414777

LEISURE CENTRE
Portslade Sport Centre
Chalky Road. Tel: (0273) 41100

STORES
Peacock Stores
17, Station Road. Tel: (0273) 414851

TAXIS
Mile Oak Taxis
19, Victoria Road. Tel: (0273) 420460
Red & White Line
56, Wolseley Road. Tel: (0273) 419740

PUNNETTS TOWN
To bely its name, this is actually a tiny hamlet in the
Weald to the east of Heathfield, near an old wind-
mill.

PUBLIC HOUSE
The Barley Mow
Tel: (0435) 830366

OTHER AMENITIES
RIDING SCHOOL
Watkins Down Riding School
Watkins Down Farm, Forest Lane.
Tel: (0435) 830235/830557

TAXI
Punnetts Town Taxis
5 Cherry Clack, North Street. Tel: (0435) 830840

RESTAURANT
The Little Chef
London Road. Tel: (079 18) 2135

RIDGEWOOD
A village to the south of Uckfield.

PUBLIC HOUSE
Highland Inn
Eastbourne Road. Tel: (0825) 762989

OTHER AMENITY
TAXI
Adams Private Car Hire
4 Council Cottages, New Road. Tel: (0825) 5902

RINGLES CROSS

RESTAURANT
Thai Fantasy Sussex Barn Restaurant
Tel: (0825) 763827

PUBLIC HOUSE
Ringles Cross
Tel: (0825) 762510

OTHER AMENITY
CAR HIRE/SELF DRIVE
Ive Drive Car & Van Hire
Ringlescross Garage. Tel: (0825) 765522/762500

RINGMER
The daughters of Ringmer have strong connections with the USA. One married William Penn,
founder of Pennsylvania, and another John Har-
vard founder of the university which bears his
name. Ringmer was also the home of Timothy, the
tortoise belonging to the famous naturalist Gilbert
White, whose shell is kept in the British Museum.
Population: 4,335.

PLACES OF INTEREST
Timothy Tortoise
Be sure to see the portrait of Timothy, Gilbert White's

famous tortoise, on the signpost at the bottom of the lane leading to the church.

HOTEL

Ringmer Inn
Lewes Road. Tel: (0273) 812348

GUEST HOUSE

Cheyney Guest House
The Green , Lewes Road. Tel: (0273) 812434

RESTAURANTS

The Anchor Inn
Lewes Road. Tel: (0273) 812370
The Cock
Uckfield Road. Tel: (0273) 812040
The Coffee House
72, Springest Avenue. Tel: (0273) 812855

PUBLIC HOUSE

The Green Man Hotel
Lewes Road. Tel: (0273) 812422

OTHER AMENITIES

FLYING SCHOOL
East Sussex Gliding Club
Clubhouse, Kitsons Field, The Broyle. Tel: (082 584) 347

SWIMMING POOL
Ringmer Swimming Pool
Ringmer County Secondary School. Tel: (0273) 813533

🐌 🐌 🐌 🐌 🐌 🐌 🐌

RIPE

A small peaceful village between Lewes and Hailsham. The church of St John the Baptist has a Pelham Tower (see East Hoathly).
Population: 552.

PUBLIC HOUSES

Barley Mow
Selmeston. Tel: (032 183) 322
The Lamb Inn
Church Lane. Tel: (032 183) 280

OTHER AMENITY

TAXI
J. West
Tel: (032 183) 337

🐌 🐌 🐌 🐌 🐌 🐌 🐌

ROBERTSBRIDGE

Originally 'Rotherbridge', this town started life as an appendage to the Cistercian abbey founded in 1176. More recently it was a junction on the Kent and East Sussex Railway, used by those hop-picking at nearby Bodiam. Originally the Rother Valley Railway, it was run by the parsimonious Colonel Stephens, the uncrowned king of small railways. The road running up from the bridge has some half-timbered houses, and alongside the green at the top of the hill is the tile-hung coaching inn, the George, where such notables as W.C. Grace and Hilaire Belloc have stayed.

RESTAURANTS

Bough House Restaurant
43 High Street. Tel: (0580) 880440
The Curlew Inn & Restaurant
Tel: (058 086) 272
Le Meridien
13 High Street. Tel: (0580) 880362
Robertsbridge Fish Farm
35 High Street. Tel: (0580) 880449

PUBLIC HOUSES

George Inn
High Street. Tel: (0580) 880315
Johns Cross Inn
Battle Road. Tel: (0580) 880257
New Eight Bells
North Bridge Street. Tel: (0580) 880722
The Ostrich Hotel
Station Road. Tel: (0580) 880264
Salehurst Halt
Church Lane. Tel: (0580) 880620

OTHER AMENITIES

CAR HIRE/SELF DRIVE
J.L.S. Self Drive
10 High Street. Tel: (0580) 880329
Johns Cross Garage
Battle Road, Johns Cross. Tel: (0580) 880222

RAILWAY STATION
British Rail
Robertsbridge Station, Station Road. Tel: (0580) 880430

TAXIS
E.J. Jaques (Robertsbridge)
1 Coronation Cottage. Tel: (0580) 880820
Robertsbridge Car Hire
5 Rutley Close. Tel: (0580) 880156
Peter Smallwood Taxis
8 Rother View. Tel: (0580) 881052

RODMELL

Virginia and Leonard Woolf owned Monks House, which is open to the public.

Population: 344.

PLACES OF INTEREST

Monks House

Country retreat of Virginia and Leonard Woolf from 1919 until his death in 1969. Open to the public in the summer. The small village house and garden is administered and maintained by tenants.

Months Open: April - October. Days Open: Wednesdays and Saturdays. Hours Open: 2 - 6pm. Admission: £1.50. Unsuitable for wheelchairs. No dogs. Maximum of 15 people in house at any one time.

PUBLIC HOUSE

The Abergavenny Arms

Newhaven Road. Tel: (0273) 472416

🙦 🙦 🙦 🙦 🙦 🙦 🙦

ROEDEAN

Renowned the length and breadth of the country for the girls' public school. The school building itself sits high on the cliffs above the sea like some gothic mansion.

CAFÉ/TEA ROOMS

Roedean Cafe

Miniature Golf Course, Marine Drive. Tel: (0273) 571513

🙦 🙦 🙦 🙦 🙦 🙦 🙦

ROTHERFIELD

Seven miles south of Tunbridge Wells, the River Rother rises in the cellar of a house here. (In true British fashion, no doubt to confuse foreigners, there are indeed two rivers called Rother, less than 20 miles apart, one in West Sussex, and one in East. If there is a reason for this eccentricity, it has remained a secret.) The town is built around an irregular crossroads, and there are some fine tile-hung houses. The church, which owes much to William Morris and Burne-Jones, unfortunately lost its spire in the 'hurricane' of October 1987.

Population: 2,957.

HOTEL

The Kings Arms

Tel: (089 285) 2465/3161

PUBLIC HOUSES

Bicycle Arms

Argos Hill. Tel: (089 285) 2855

The Catts Inn

Tel: (089 285) 2546

The George Inn

Church Road. Tel: (089 285) 2474

The Harvest Moon

Yew Tree Lane. Tel: (089 285) 2516

OTHER AMENITIES

CAR HIRE/SELF DRIVE

Kennedy Bros. (Engineers) Ltd.

North Street. TN6 3LY Tel: (089 285) 2286

RIDING SCHOOLS

Treblers Livery

Treblers Road. Tel: (0892) 661509

P.F. Whittington

Heathfield Hall, Town Row. Tel: (089 285) 2359

TAXI

B & J Taxis

Asmara, 2 Ridgemont, Station Road. Tel: (089 285) 3217

🙦 🙦 🙦 🙦 🙦 🙦 🙦

ROTTINGDEAN

A very pretty village, with fine Georgian houses grouped around a village green and duckpond. Built in a gap in the downs between Brighton and Newhaven on the coast, Rottingdean has inevitably had a history of smuggling. The Duke of Wellington went to school here, the artist Burne-Jones had a fine house here and Kipling did much of his best writing here before retiring to Batemans at Burwash.

Population: 8,676.

PLACES OF INTEREST

Grange Art Gallery & Museum

Tel: (0273) 301004

The Georgian house, adjacent to Kipling's home, displays illustrations, letters and books of the author. Frequent temporary displays. Toys from the toy museum.

Months Open: All year. Days Open: Monday - Sunday (Closed Wednesday). Hours Open: Mon, Thurs, Sat 10am - 5pm; Tues, Fri 10am - 1pm, 2 - 5pm; Sun 2 - 5. Bank Holidays: Open (except December 25, 26, January 1, Good Friday). Admission: Free.

HOTELS

The Olde Place Hotel

High Street. Tel: (0273) 301051

The White Horse Hotel

Marine Drive. Tel: (0273) 300301

ROTTINGDEAN GREEN

GUEST HOUSES

Braemar House
Steyning Road. Tel: (0273) 34263
Corner House
Steyning Road. Tel: (0273) 34533

RESTAURANTS

The Coach House
24, High Street. Tel: (0273) 301945
The Coffee Mill
55, Marine Drive. Tel: (0273) 305894
The Passage to India
30, High Street. Tel: (0273) 302067
Pizzeria Umberto
74, High Street. Tel: (0273) 35972
The Plough Inn
Vicarage Lane. Tel: (0273) 35805
Smiths Restaurant
14, Nevill Road. Tel: (0273) 37585

PUBLIC HOUSE

The Black Horse
High Street. Tel: (0273) 32581

CAFÉS & TEA ROOMS

Old Cottage
62, High Street. Tel: (0273) 33426
Rottingdean Patisserie
32, High Street. Tel: (0273) 32180

OTHER AMENITY

HEALTH CLUB
Unit One Sauna
St. Margaret's High Street. Tel: (0273) 37253

ᨳ ᨳ ᨳ ᨳ ᨳ ᨳ ᨳ

RUSHLAKE GREEN

A part of the parish of Warbleton, in the Weald south-east of Heathfield.

PUBLIC HOUSES

Horse & Groom Inn
The Green. Tel: (0435) 830320
Three Cups Inn
Three Cups. Tel: (0435) 830252

ᨳ ᨳ ᨳ ᨳ ᨳ ᨳ ᨳ

RYE TOWN TAKEN FROM THE CHURCH TOWER

RYE

Probably the Jewel in the Crown of East Sussex. It has been suggested that if it hadn't existed, Rye would have to have been created to satisfy the tourist industry. Coachloads of tourists are drawn to this ancient and historic royal borough every year, particularly in summer. The most impressive of the three Sussex hill towns, (Lewes and Winchelsea are the others), Rye is as beautiful at a distance as it is close up. The 12th century church, St Mary, dominates the summit of the sandstone hill that rises out of the flat fens around, and the streets, some of them cobbled, radiate from it. There are some fine houses and inns, and one, the Mermaid, is probably the most photogenic in the country. Rye was one of the Cinque Ports, although not a full member until 1336. The town suffered a tempestuous time at the hands of the marauding French, who three times sacked the town, most disastrously in 1448, burning it to the ground. Storms and the silted-up harbour further restricted Rye's growth as a port, but it became notorious in the 17th and 18th century as a centre for highly profitable smuggling. The houses, with their deeply vaulted cellars and interconnecting attics, were ideal for the purpose. John Wesley preached to the people of Rye in 1773, who were willing enough to listen to him, but were not prepared to forego 'the accursed thing smuggling'. The American novelist Henry James fell in love with Rye, and he lived and wrote at Lambs House (National Trust). Many of his countrymen still come to share his enthusiasm. *Population: 4,704.*

PLACES OF INTEREST

Lamb House

West Street.

A Georgian house and garden, home of Henry James from 1898-1916. Some of his furniture and personal possessions on view.

Months Open: April - October. Days Open: Wednesday & Saturdays only. Hours Open: 2 - 6pm. Admission: £1.00. No lavatories. No dogs. Unsuitable for wheelchairs.

Rye Museum

Tel: (0797) 223454

Local collections housed in a 13th century tower. Pottery from the Rye Kilns, toys and dolls.

Months Open: Easter - October. Days Open: Every day. Hours

MERMAID STREET, RYE

Open: Mon - Sat 10.30am - 1pm, 2.15 - 5.30pm; Sun 11.30am - 1pm, 2.15 - 5.30pm.

Rye Town Museum

Tel: (0797) 223902

The fascinating history of Rye, shown in a theatrical light and sound show. Ten shows a day.

Months Open: Easter - November. Visitor shop and local exhibitions.

HOTELS

Cinque Ports Hotel

Cinque Ports Street. Tel: (0797) 222319

The Crown Hotel

Ferry Road. Tel: (0797) 223372

Durrant House Hotel

East Street. Tel: (0797) 223182

A spacious Georgian residence set in the centre of 13th

DURRANT HOUSE HOTEL

century Rye which possesses much history, character and charm, this family-run hotel is well known for its five course table d'hôte evening dinners, fine wines, and very friendly atmosphere.

BEDROOMS: 10 Double, (10 en suite, 10 TV, 10 tea/coffee) B&B £ 32.00 - £ 42.00. 3 Twin, (3 en suite, 3 TV, 3 tea/coffee) B&B £ 30.00 - £ 42.00. 2 Family, (2 en suite, 2 TV, 2 tea/coffee) £ 39.00–£ 58.00. 1 Four Poster £ 50.00. 1 Suite. RESTAURANT: Varied Cuisine. Credit Cards: Ac. Am. D. V.

Weekend Breaks: 2 nights: £ 60.00. 3 nights: £ 80.00.

George Hotel
High Street. Tel: (0797) 222114

Hope Anchor Hotel
Watchbell Street. Tel: (0797) 222216/223973
A delightful 17th century hotel situated at the end of a cobbled street with magnificent views of the countryside surrounding Rye.

BEDROOMS: 1 Single (1 TV, 1 tea/coffee) B&B £ 33.00. 5 Double (3 en suite, 5 TV, 5 tea/coffee) B&B £ 48.00 - £ 55.00. 5 Twin (3 en suite, 5 TV, 5 tea/coffee) B&B £ 48.00 - £ 55.00. 1 Family (1 TV, 1 tea/coffee) RESTAURANT: English Cuisine. Dinner: £ 10.00. House Wine: £ 6.50. À La Carte: £ 12.00. Specialities: Fresh local fish dishes. Credit Cards: Ac.

Weekend Breaks: 2 nights: £ 70.00. 3 nights: £ 105.00. Allowance towards dinner: £ 10.00.

Mariners Hotel
15 High Street. Tel: (0797) 223480/222183

Mermaid Hotel
Mermaid Street. Tel: (0797) 223065/222389

The Old Borough Arms
The Strand. Tel: (0797) 222128

Queens Head Hotel
Landgate. Tel: (0797) 222181

The Regent Motel
42 Cinque Ports Street. Tel: (0797) 225884

GUEST HOUSES

Aviemore Guest House
28 Fishmarket Road. Tel: (0797) 223052

Jeakes Guest House

Mermaid Street. Tel: (0797) 222828

Little Saltcote Guest House
22 Military Road. Tel: (0797) 223210

The Old Vicarage Hotel & Restaurant
15 East Street. Tel: (0797) 225131/222119

The Windmill Guest House
Ferry Road. Tel: (0797) 224027

RESTAURANTS

Casa Conti
108 High Street. Tel: (0797) 222574

Chez Dominique
6 Tower Street. Tel: (0797) 222174

Copper Kettle Restaurant
34 The Mint. Tel: (0797) 222012

Elizabethan Restaurant
Cinque Ports Street. Tel: (0797) 223091

The Fish Shop
37 The Mint. Tel: (0797) 223268

Flushing Inn
Market Street. Tel: (0797) 223292

Holloway House
24 High Street. Tel: (0797) 224748

Kettle of Fish
25 Wish Street. Tel: (0797) 223684

Landgate Bistro
5/6 Landgate. Tel: (0797) 222829

Ma Beeton's Restaurant
36/38 Cinque Ports Street. Tel: (0797) 222262

The Mayflower Restaurant
2 High Street. Tel: (0797) 223360

The Monastery
6 High Street. Tel: (0797) 223272

Monrow's Restaurant
14 Cinque Ports Street. Tel: (0797) 224294

Old Forge Restaurant
Wish Street. Tel: (0797) 223227

Quayhole Restaurant
Strand Quay. Tel: (0797) 223638

The Runcible Spoon
62 Cinque Ports Street. Tel: (0797) 225094

Shades Coffee Shop
7 High Street. Tel: (0797) 223983

Simmons Restaurant
35 High Street. Tel: (0797) 222026/222207

Wing Wah
17 Landgate. Tel: (0797) 223289

PUBLIC HOUSES

The Bedford Arms
Bedford Place, Fishmarket Road. Tel: (0797) 223005

The Bell Inn
High Street. Tel: (0797) 223323

Ferry Boat Inn

RYE HARBOUR

Ferry Road. Tel: (0797) 223027
The Globe Inn
10 Military Road. Tel: (0797) 222180
Ye Olde Pipemakers Arms
Wish Ward. Tel: (0797) 223064
The Queen Adelaide
Ferry Road. Tel: (0797) 223135
The Standard Inn
The Mint. Tel: (0797) 223393
The Top O The Hill
Rye Hill. Tel: (0797) 223284
Union Inn
East Street. Tel: (0797) 222334
Ypres Castle Inn
Gun Gardens, Church Square. Tel: (0797) 223248

CAFÉS & TEA ROOMS

Fletchers House
Lion Street. Tel: (0797) 223101
Ice Box
60 Cinque Port Street. Tel: (0797) 224805

OTHER AMENITIES

ART GALLERIES

Easton Rooms Gallery
107 High Street. Tel: (0797) 222433
Kurrein Gallery
7 Lion Street. Tel: (0797) 223383
The Mint Gallery
77a High Street. Tel: (0797) 222943

ART GALLERY

Rye Art Gallery (Stormont Bequest)
Ypres Studio, East Street. Tel: (0797) 223218

BUS & COACH SERVICES

Hastings & District Transport Ltd.
Station Road. Tel: (0797) 223343

CAR HIRE/SELF DRIVE

Paine of Rye
The Drive, Shipyard Lane. TN31 7HL Tel: (0797) 223095
Skinners (Rye) Ltd
74 Fishmarket Road. Tel: (0797) 223334

CARAVAN PARK
Frenchmans Beach Caravan Park
Rye Harbour Road. Tel: (0797) 223011

HOSPITAL
Mill House Hospital
Rye Hill. Tel: (0797) 223001

LEISURE CENTRE
Castle Water Estate
Rye Harbour Road. Tel: (0797) 224652

RIDING SCHOOL
Watlands Livery Stables
Udimore Road. Tel: (0797) 222506

STORES
Woolworths plc
High Street. Tel: (0797) 222335

TAXIS
Petes Cabs
6 Fishmarket Road. Tel: (0797) 225028
Rother Cabs
Tel: (0797) 224554
Rye Motors
57 Winchelsea Road. Tel: (0797) 223176
Taxi-Time
6 Mary Stanford Green. Tel: (0797) 224016
Taxi and private hire
Months Open: January to December. Days Open: Monday-Saturday and some Sundays. Hours Open: 8am - 10pm. Bank holidays by arrangement. Long distance. Airports/docks. Tours and day trips. Mercedes/Volvo luxury saloon cars. Rates: Variable by hour or mile.. Proprietor: David Robus.
Colin Walker
15 Bankside. Tel: (0797) 224233

WATER SPORTS
Castle Water Estate Company
Castle Water Cottage, Rye Harbour Road.
Tel: (0797) 223720

☙ ☙ ☙ ☙ ☙ ☙ ☙

RYE FOREIGN

A small village a couple of miles outside Rye so named when it was inhabited by Huguenouts fleeing from persecution in France in the 17th century.

HOTEL
Broomhill Lodge Hotel
Tel: (079 78) 421

RYE HARBOUR

Boats used to go right up into the town itself, but now the modern harbour is some distance away, along a road lined with gravel pits. It lacks the charm of Rye.

RESTAURANT
Inkerman Arms
Tel: (0797) 222464

PUBLIC HOUSE
William The Conqueror
Tel: (0797) 223315

OTHER AMENITY
TAXI
Taxi-Time
6 Mary Stanford Green. Tel: (0797) 224016

☙ ☙ ☙ ☙ ☙ ☙ ☙

SALTDEAN

The hamlet dates from 1934; the Butlin's camp from 1938.

PLACES OF INTEREST
Butlin's & The Lido
Both quaint examples of '30s futuristic architecture. Thankfully the future didn't turn out that way.

HOTELS
Linbrook Lodge Hotel
74, Lenham Avenue. Tel: (0273) 303775
Ocean Hotel
Longridge Avenue. Tel: (0273) 302291

RESTAURANT
The Wonkey Donkey
140, Saltdean Vale. Tel: (0273) 33816

OTHER AMENITIES
TAXIS
Mar Taxis
53, Longridge Avenue. Tel: (0273) 300624
Saltdean Mini Coach & Taxi Service
38, Shepham Avenue. Tel: (0273) 37236

WINE BAR
Gullen's Coffee Lounge
67, Longridge Avenue. Tel: (0273) 32564

☙ ☙ ☙ ☙ ☙ ☙ ☙

ANY DESTINATION
TAXI & PRIVATE HIRE CONTRACTS

TAXI - TIME

PHONE DAVE ROBUS

RYE:(0797) 224016

Advance enquiries and bookings accepted with pleasure

URGENT CALLS CAR PHONE: (0860) 419922

Sightseeing Trips, Long Distances and Tours planned for your requirements. Any driving job carried out by careful, professional drivers.
Mercedes/Volvo Saloons.
Chauffeur your own car service.
Licensed, Safe, Reliable Taxi and
Private Hire Contracts.
Urgent/fast Delivery and Courier Work.
GATWICK - HEATHROW - CHANNEL FERRY -
LONDON SPECIALISTS

Safe & Reliable Travel
EXECUTIVE & LUXURY TRAVEL SPECIALISTS

THE SEVEN SISTERS FROM SEAFORD HEAD

SEAFORD

Originally standing at the mouth of the Ouse, Seaford was the medieval port for Lewes. When the 'new haven' took over that role, Seaford became a sleepy village, then gradually grew into a seaside resort, and now comprising genteel housing estates , private schools and golf courses.

PLACES OF INTEREST

Seaford Museum of Local History
No. 74 Martello Tower, Esplanade.
Tel: (0323) 893976
Period TV, radio, domestic appliances, photographs. "A trip down memory lane".
Months Open: Summer and Winter. Days Open: Summer: Sun, Wed, Sat; Winter: Sundays. Hours Open: Summer: 2.30 - 4.30pm; Winter: 11am - 1pm, 2.30 - 4.30pm. Parties by appointment only.

HOTELS

Abbots Lodge Motor Inn
Station Road. BN25 2RB. Tel: (0323) 891055
Avondale Hotel
Avondale Road. Tel: (0323) 890008

Clearview Hotel
38, Claremont Road. Tel: (0323) 890138
New Beach Hotel
18, The Esplanade. Tel: (0323) 892497
The Old Plough Inn
20, Church Street. Tel: (0323) 892379
The Royal Duke Hotel
7, Dane Road. Tel: (0323) 892354
Seaford Head Hotel
Tel: (0323) 893241
The Wellington Hotel
Steyne Road. Tel: (0323) 890032
The White Lion Hotel
74, Claremont Road. Tel: (0323) 892473

GUEST HOUSES

Bentley Guest House
23, Pelham Road. Tel: (0323) 893171
Castleton Guest House
34, Claremont Road. Tel: (0323) 892380
High Beach Guest House
Marine Parade. Tel: (0323) 892287
Traslyn Guest House
Pelham Road. Tel: (0323) 892312

RESTAURANTS

Dunkies
7, Sutton Park Road. Tel: (0323) 895508

La Mer Restaurant
8, Church Street. Tel: (0323) 894477

Moon of India
18, Sutton Park Road. Tel: (0323) 892406

The Pizza Connection
4, Claremont Road. Tel: (0323) 890711
Pizza and pastas Cuisine.

The Regency Restaurant
20, High Street. Tel: (0323) 895206

The Salad Bowl
21, High Street. Tel: (0323) 890605

Seaford Steak House
11, Clinton Place. Tel: (0323) 893529

Tangs Chinese Restaurant
42, Broad Street. Tel: (0323) 890150

Taste of India Restaurant
30, Church Street. Tel: (0323) 899077

PUBLIC HOUSES

Beachcomber Free House Hotel
Dane Road. Tel: (0323) 892719

Buckle Inn
Marine Parade. Tel: (0323) 893356

The Chequers Inn
49, High Street. Tel: (0323) 892381

The Crown Inn
Church Road. Tel: (0323) 892307

The Hole In The Wall
Pelham Yard, High Street. Tel: (0323) 893785

The Lord Admiral
Pelham Road. Tel: (0323) 891671

The Seven Sisters
Alfriston Road. Tel: (0323) 896548

CAFÉ/TEA ROOMS

The Tuck Inn
5, South Street. Tel: (0323) 896581

OTHER AMENITIES

ART GALLERY
The Steyne Gallery
1, High Street. Tel: (0323) 891178

CAR HIRE
Blatchington Motors
Blatchington Road. Tel: (0323) 892745

Keith Davies
20, Rochford Way. Tel: (0323) 896785

G. Carter Cars
The Corner, Claremont Road. Tel: (0323) 896890

CARAVAN PARKS

The Buckle Caravan & Camping Park
Marine Parade. Tel: (0323) 897801
Touring caravan park
Months Open: 1 March-31 October. Days Open: 7 days a week.
Hours Open: 8.30am-8.30pm. Open all Bank Holidays. Proprietor: Mr D Perry.

Sunnyside Caravan Park
Marine Parade. Tel: (0323) 892825

GARDEN CENTRE
Bishopstone Nurseries
Norton. Tel: (0323) 892895

HEALTH CLUB
Grahams Gym
1a, Blatchington Road. Tel: (0323) 894033

LEISURE CENTRE
Downs Leisure Centre
Sutton Road. Tel: (0323) 490011

RAILWAY STATION
Seaford Station
Station Approach. Tel: (0323) 892151

STORES
Woolworths Plc
Broad Street. Tel: (0323) 893614

TAXIS
Carlton Taxi Services
3a, Broad Street. Tel: (0323) 894441

Cox's Taxis
7a, Clinton Place. Tel: (0323) 893301

J & S Taxis
9, Alfriston Road. Tel: (0323) 890124

Link Taxis
The Drive. Tel: (0323) 891615

P.D.Taxis
3a, Broad Street. Tel: (0323) 893122

Ranks
Seaford Station. Tel: (0323) 893414

C.F. Rigesford
15, Sandgate Close. Tel: (0323) 892143

Silver Streak Radio Taxis
21a, High Street. Tel: (0323) 892782/894685

WINE BAR
Flintstones Wine Bar
Saxon Lane. Tel: (0323) 892278

🐾 🐾 🐾 🐾 🐾 🐾 🐾

SHEFFIELD PARK GARDEN

SEDLESCOMBE

A pretty village that has a long narrow village green with a well-house like a market cross, and a selection of tearooms and antique shops. Stone was transported from here along the River Brede during the construction of Battle Abbey, and more recently there were several large ironworks. Now Sedlescombe is most renowned for the Pestalozzi Children's Village nearby, founded at the turn of the century, where disaffected children from around the world receive a proper grounding in life.

Population: 1,256.

HOTEL
Brickwall Hotel
The Green. Tel: (042 487) 253/339

RESTAURANTS
Holmes House Restaurant
The Green. Tel: (042 487) 450
Tithe Barn Restaurant
Tithe Barn, Lower Green. Tel: (042 487) 393
The Waterfall
The Street. TN33 0QB Tel: (042 487) 273

PUBLIC HOUSES
Coach & Horses
Tel: (042 487) 204
Queens Head Hotel
The Green. Tel: (042 487) 228

OTHER AMENITY
GARDEN CENTRE
Blackbrooks Garden Centre
A21. Tel: (0424) 870710/870673

❧ ❧ ❧ ❧ ❧ ❧ ❧

SELMESTON

A tiny village midway between Lewes and Eastbourne, site of a Neolithic causewayed camp circa 3000BC.

RESTAURANT
Silletts Cottage Restaurant
Church Farm. Tel: (032 183) 343
English & continental Cuisine. Specialities: Fresh fish, fresh meat, oven casseroles. Hours Open: Lunch: 12.00-2.00. Dinner: 7.00-10.30. OpenSundays. Dinner: £ 15.95. House Wine: £ 6.25. Credit Cards: Ac. V. Seating Capacity: 45. Outdoor eating. No pipes or cigars Areas: Veg. W/chair acc. P. W. Reco: M*

SHEFFIELD GREEN

Half a mile west of the A 275, and just north of Sheffield Park, close to the county border.

RESTAURANT
The Sheffield Coach House
A275 Lewes Road. Tel: (0825) 790245

🍂 🍂 🍂 🍂 🍂 🍂 🍂

SHEFFIELD PARK

Now most renowned for its wonderful gardens, the house, which is not open to the public, has played host to a number of interesting Englishmen. The Earl of Sheffield of the 1890s was a keen cricketer, and the Australian tourists of the day would play their opening match here. Edward Gibbon who wrote 'The Decline and Fall of the Roman Empire' spent his last days here. The gardens were laid out by the hard-working Capability Brown (although some say Repton). Unfortunately they were badly savaged by the hurricane of October 1987, but are splendid none the less, with a huge variety of trees.

PLACES OF INTEREST
Bluebell Railway
Tel: (082572) 2370
Sheffield Park Station is the southern terminus of the lovingly resurrected Bluebell Line, and has been restored in the lineage of London, Brighton and South Coast Railway(LBSCR).This living museum operates vintage steam trains between Sheffield Park and Horsted Keynes. *Months Open: Spring and Autumn; All year on Sundays. Days Open: Saturdays and Sundays. Buffet, museum, shop and car parking.*
Sheffield Park Garden
Tel: (0825) 790655
Large gardens with a series of lakes linked by cascades; large variety of unusual shrubs. *Months Open: March - November. Days Open: Tuesdays - Saturdays. Hours Open: 11am - 6pm (sunset if earlier). Bank Holidays: 2 - 6pm. Admission: £2.80. Children half price. Closed Tuesdays following Bank Holidays. No dogs.*

GUEST HOUSE
Northlands Farm House
Ketches Lane. Tel: (0825) 790958

🍂 🍂 🍂 🍂 🍂 🍂 🍂

SHORTGATE

A tiny hamlet in the flat water-crossed plain northwest of Lewes.

PUBLIC HOUSE
Blue Bell Inn
Lewes Road. Tel: (082 584) 315

🍂 🍂 🍂 🍂 🍂 🍂 🍂

SIDLEY

The northern suburb of Bexhill, with a late Victorian church.

HOTEL
Pelham Hotel
Holliers Hill. Tel: (0424) 210269

PUBLIC HOUSES
The New Inn
32 Ninefield Road. Tel: (0424) 210581
Sussex Hotel
Ninfield Road. Tel: (0424) 222413

OTHER AMENITY
TAXI
W.A. Clifton
4 Canada Way. Tel: (0424) 215855

🍂 🍂 🍂 🍂 🍂 🍂 🍂

SILVERHILL

A high part of Hastings that once boasted a windmill. St Matthews is an Early English red brick church, with 13th century origins. *Population: 4,804.*

PUBLIC HOUSES
The Duke
Duke Road. Tel: (0424) 436241
White Horse Inn
London Road. Tel: (058 086) 235

OTHER AMENITY
BUS & COACH SERVICES
Hastings & District Transport Ltd.
Beaufort Road. Tel: (0424) 433711

🍂 🍂 🍂 🍂 🍂 🍂 🍂

SOUTH CHAILEY

See Chailey.

PUBLIC HOUSES
The Horns Lodge
South Street. Tel: (0273) 400422
The Swan Inn
South Common. Tel: (0273) 400459

OTHER AMENITIES

HOSPITAL
Pouchlands Hospital
Mill Lane. Tel: (0273) 890444

TAXI
Chailey Cars
11, Kilmwood Lane. Tel: (0273) 400182

🐚 🐚 🐚 🐚 🐚 🐚 🐚

SOUTH HEIGHTON
Now almost indistinguishable from Denton.
Population: 939.

PUBLIC HOUSE
The Hampden Arms
Heighton Road. Tel: (0273) 514529

OTHER AMENITIES
CARAVAN PARK
Hampden Vale Caravan Centre
Tel: (0273) 513530

TAXI
Leons Taxis
2, Cottage Close. Tel: (0273) 515104

🐚 🐚 🐚 🐚 🐚 🐚 🐚

SOUTHWICK
A part of the urban sprawl that links Shoreham with Brighton.

RESTAURANTS
The Grange Restaurant
9, Southwick Square. Tel: (0273) 593872
Waves Restaurant & Bar
Lady Bee Marina , Albion Street. Tel: (0273) 597422

PUBLIC HOUSES
The Cricketers
18, The Green. Tel: (0273) 592081
The Pilot
Station Road. Tel: (0273) 591789
Romans Hotel
Manor Hall Road. Tel: (0273) 592147
The Royal George
Upper Shoreham Road. Tel: (0273) 591904
The Schooner Hotel
Albion Street. Tel: (0273) 592252
The Windmill Inn
180, Old Shoreham Road. Tel: (0273) 592309

OTHER AMENITIES

CAR HIRE
Flaxley Cabs
178, Old Shoreham Road. Tel: (0273) 591834
Woolworths Plc
Southwick Square. Tel: (0273) 594585

TAXI
Southwick Cabs
132, Albion Street. Tel: (0273) 410630

THEATRE
Barn Theatre
Community Centre , Southwick Street.
Tel: (0273) 597094

🐚 🐚 🐚 🐚 🐚 🐚 🐚

ST. LEONARDS-ON-SEA
On the western side of Hastings, St Leonards is a totally manufactured place, the inspiration of one man, James Burton, and his son Decimus. It was he who designed much of Regents Park, and the style is echoed with Greek columns in front of many of the buildings.
Population: 3,898.

HOTELS
Beauport Park Hotel
Battle Road. TN38 8EA. Tel: (0424) 51222
The Bo-Peep Hotel
West Marina. Tel: (0424) 427371
The Chimes Hotel
1 St. Matthews Gardens. Tel: (0424) 434041/420681
Clevedon Court Hotel
51 Warrior Square. Tel: (0424) 423377/433399
Derwent Hotel
38 Sedlescombe Road South. Tel: (0424) 436044
The Drayton Hotel
30-31 Eversfield Place. Tel: (0424) 420087/424742
Eagle House Hotel
12 Pevensey Road. Tel: (0424) 430535/441273
Falcon Hotel
29 Eversfield Place. Tel: (0424) 424005
Grand Hotel
Grand Parade. TN38 0DD. Tel: (0424) 428510
The Highlands Hotel
Boscobel Road. Tel: (0424) 420299
Mayfair Hotel
9 Eversfield Place. Tel: (0424) 434061
Pinehurst Hotel
3 Avondale Road. Tel: (0424) 423687
Randolph Hotel

7 Eversfield Place. Tel: (0424) 422347
Regent Hotel
13/15 Eversfield Place. Tel: (0424) 432223
Royal Victoria Hotel
The Marina. Tel: (0424) 445544
William the Conqueror Hotel
28 Eversfield Place. Tel: (0424) 420444
Windsor Hotel
9 Warrior Square. Tel: (0424) 422709

GUEST HOUSES
Adelphi Methodist Hotel
Warrior Square. Tel: (0424) 437622/429750
Campbell Guest House
143 Marina. Tel: (0424) 425793
Egmonds Guest House & Restaurant
21 Grand Parade. Tel: (0424) 437000
High Toby Guesthouse
21 Magdalen Road. Tel: (0424) 431908
The Kings Road Hotel
52 Kings Road. Tel: (0424) 430733
Living Water Christian Guest House
19 St. Margarets Road. Tel: (0424) 421455
Loretto
22 Warrior Gardens. Tel: (0424) 439419
Rutland Guest House
17 Grosvenor Crescent. Tel: (0424) 714720
Tower Guest House
28 Tower Road West. Tel: (0424) 427217

RESTAURANTS
Aphrodite's Taverna
65/66 Eversfield Place. TN37 6DB Tel: (0424) 439088
C & K Fish Bar
23 Bexhill Road. Tel: (0424) 428699
China Kitchen
30 Tower Road. Tel: (0424) 435279
Companion House
96 Norman Road. Tel: (0424) 437736
Cypriana
393 London Road. Tel: (0424) 411939
E & B Fishbar
117 Bohemia Road. Tel: (0424) 426348
Efes Kebab & Pizza
19a Bexhill Road. Tel: (0424) 445927
Golden Fry
101 Battle Road. Tel: (0424) 430492
Hung Tao Chinese Restaurant
18 Kings Road. Tel: (0424) 431757
Karpasiana Restaurant
24 Grosvenor Crescent. Tel: (0424) 428529
Kings Fish Bar & Restaurant
16 Kings Road. Tel: (0424) 427906
La Cuisine

11 Grand Parade. TN38 0DD Tel: (0424) 437589
La Rustica
316 Bexhill Road. Tel: (0424) 424930
Lotus Chinese Restaurant & Take Away
13 Grand Parade. TN38 0HF Tel: (0424) 420115
Marvans Restaurant
29 London Road. Tel: (0424) 435728
Pasta Pasta
8 Grand Parade. Tel: (0424) 423608
Italian Cuisine. Specialities: Pasta and salad bar. Last Orders: 11pm. Open Sundays. Credit Cards: Ac. V. Seating Capacity: 50. Veg.
Patricia's Catering
3 Eversfield Place. Tel: (0424) 717329
Positano Restaurant
7 Marine Court. Tel: (0424) 433464
Roser's
64 Eversfield Place. TN37 6DB Tel: (0424) 712218
The Royal
1 St. Johns Road. Tel: (0424) 420147
Ruby's Chinese Takeaway
60 Battle Road. Tel: (0424) 439053
Sea View Restaurant
9 Norman Road. Tel: (0424) 535366/445822
Shiplu Tandoori Restaurant
5 Norman Road. Tel: (0424) 439273
Indian Cuisine. Last Orders: 11.45pm. Closed 2.30pm-6.00pm. Credit Cards: Ac. Am. D. V. Seating Capacity: 36. Veg. W/chair
Silver River
56 Bohemia Road. Tel: (0424) 433439
Silver Valley
47 Sedlescombe Road North. Tel: (0424) 435710
Silverhill Indian Tandoori Restaurant
375 London Road. Tel: (0424) 439436
Indian Cuisine. Specialities: Chicken Tikka Masala, Lamb Pasanda, Chicken Pasanda. Hours Open: Lunch: 12.00-2.15. Dinner: 6.00-12.00. Last Orders: midnight. Closed 2.15-6.00pm. Open Sundays. Credit Cards: Ac. Am. V. Seating Capacity: 40. Veg. P.
Johnny Swan
40 Kings Road. Tel: (0424) 427619
Taffys Fish Bar
211 Bexhill Road. Tel: (0424) 426141
The Tudor Tryst
54 Kings Road. Tel: (0424) 423008
Turners Restaurant
57 Norman Road. Tel: (0424) 722226

PUBLIC HOUSES
The Bull Inn
530 Bexhill Road. Tel: (0424) 424984
The Bulverhythe Hotel
311 Bexhill Road. Tel: (0424) 420513
The Clarence

389 London Road. Tel: (0424) 422514
The Clifton Tavern
1/2 Stainsby Street. Tel: (0424) 421341
The Comet
Harley Shute Road. Tel: (0424) 439117
The Dripping Spring
Tower Road. Tel: (0424) 434055
Hollington Oak Hotel
Wishing Tree Road. Tel: (0424) 424104
The Horse & Groom
East Ascent. Tel: (0424) 420612
James Burton Free House
42/43 Marina. Tel: (0424) 422705
Marina Inn
Caves Road. Tel: (0424) 420235
The Norman Arms
Norman Road. Tel: (0424) 420827
The North Star
Clarence Road. Tel: (0424) 439485
Old England Public House
45 London Road. Tel: (0424) 428654
Railway Hotel
1 Kings Road. Tel: (0424) 43560
The Royal
1 St. Johns Road. Tel: (0424) 420147
Tivoli Tavern
Battle Road. Tel: (0424) 429760
The Tower Hotel
251 London Road. Tel: (0424) 430225
The Warriors Gate
London Road. Tel: (0424) 424806
The Welcome Stranger
55 Seddlescombe Road North. Tel: (0424) 423180
The Wheatsheaf
172 Bohemia Road. Tel: (0424) 429679
Wishing Tree
Wishing Tree Road. Tel: (0424) 51473
Yorkshire Grey
2 London Road. Tel: (0424) 420711

CAFÉS & TEA ROOMS

499 Cafe
499 Bexhill Road. Tel: (0424) 420072
Bettys Pantry
87 Bohemia Road. Tel: (0424) 432038
Doano's Cafe
13 Grand Parade. Tel: (0424) 420115
Fairlands Transport Cafe
405 Bexhill Road. Tel: (0424) 435306
G.A. Forte
2 Eversfield Place. Tel: (0424) 425569
A.H. Hamed
3 London Road. Tel: (0424) 420279
The Hive Cafe
21 London Road. Tel: (0424) 430501
108

OTHER AMENITIES

ART GALLERY
Galleria Fine Arts
77 Norman Road. TN38 8EG Tel: (0424) 722317

ART GALLERIES
Photogallery
Foresters Arms, 2 Shepherd Street. Tel: (0424) 440140
Popular Originals
9 Marine Court. Tel: (0424) 722304

BUS & COACH SERVICES
Top Line Buses
Whitworth Road. Tel: (0424) 753766

CAR HIRE/CHAUFFEUR DRIVEN
Regency Cars
33 Brittany Road. Tel: (0424) 442053

CAR HIRE/SELF DRIVE
A & K Private Hire
99 Battle Road. Tel: (0424) 431831
B.V.H. Ltd.
105 Battle Road. Tel: (0424) 428121
Coombs
36-39 Western Road. Tel: (0424) 424545
Greenhalf Self Drive
Grand Parade Garage, 1/7 Market Street. Tel: (0424) 420370
Self drive hire and garage
Months Open: All year. Days Open: Mon-Fri, Sat am only.
Hours Open: 8.00am-12.30pm/2.00pm-5.30pm. Bank Holidays by arrangement only. 24 latest model Ford cars and light vans. Escort Mk 4 s, Fiestas, Sierras, estates and automatics. Full garage services and repair facilities. Proprietors: John and Guy Greenhalf
Motorhaven Self Drive Hire
Bexhill Road. Tel: (0424) 420660
Skinners (St. Leonards) Ltd.
5 Western Road. Tel: (0424) 212001/212000

CARAVAN PARKS
Beauport Caravan Park
The Ridge West. Tel: (0424) 51246/52056
Combe Haven Holiday Park
Harley Shute Road. Tel: (0424) 427891
Harrow Caravan Park
Summerhills, Harrow Lane. Tel: (0424) 751785

GARDEN CENTRES
Filsham Nurseries
37 Charles Road West, (off The Green). Tel: (0424) 421663
F. Strickland & Sons

35 Sedlescombe Road North. Tel: (0424) 423348

HEALTH CLUB
Atlantic Centre
15/17 South Street. Tel: (0424) 441264

HOSPITAL
Buchanan Hospital
Springfield Road. Tel: (0424) 422666

RIDING SCHOOLS
Beauport Park Riding School
The Ridge West. TN38 8EA Tel: (0424) 51424
B. North
Hyfield Farm, Swainham Lane. Tel: (042 483) 416

SAUNA
Todd's Solarium & Sauna
66 Battle Road. Tel: (0424) 424586

TAXIS
Abba Taxis
2A Silchester Road. Tel: (0424) 434296
Carney's Cars
94 Marina. Tel: (0424) 722067
Dial-A-Cab
6 Hollybank Gardens. Tel: (0424) 433987
Langham Taxis
257 Sedlescombe Road North. Tel: (0424) 753155
Thomas's Radio Cabs
1 Marine. Tel: (0424) 435777/424216/424399
Taxi
Months Open: Jan-Dec. Days Open: 7 days. Hours Open: 7am-1am Sun-Thur, 7am-3pm Fri, Sat. Open all Bank Holidays. Rates: As per Hastings Borough Council.
Vine Car Service
56 Tower Road West. Tel: (0424) 423317

ða ða ða ða ða ða ða

STANMER
The University of Sussex is built in Stanmer Park, on the outskirts of Brighton. The village, set in the park is quaint, but will be less so when the by-pass roars by in a few years time.

ða ða ða ða ða ða ða

STAPLECROSS

PUBLIC HOUSE
The Cross Inn
Tel: (058 083) 217

STONE CROSS
On the northern approach to Eastbourne from Hailsham, just west of the Pevensey Levels. There is a partly preserved windmill here.

HOTEL
The Red Lion Hotel
Lion Hill. Tel: (0323) 761468

PUBLIC HOUSE
Coopers Free House
Hailsham Road. Tel: (0323) 763212

OTHER AMENITY
GARDEN CENTRE
Stone Cross Nurseries & Garden Centre
A27, Battle Road. Tel: (0323) 763250

ða ða ða ða ða ða ða

STONEGATE
In the north-east part of the county, south of Tunbridge Wells, this tiny hamlet is set around a minor crossroads. St Peter's church has a weatherboard spire.

RESTAURANT
Inn on the Tracks
Tel: (0435) 883243

OTHER AMENITY
TAXI
Bob's Cars
Battenhurst Farm. Tel: (0435) 882884

ða ða ða ða ða ða ða

TARRING NEVILLE
The church contains an iron chest from one of the ships of the Spanish Armada.
Population: 30.

ða ða ða ða ða ða ða

TELHAM
Small village outside Battle.

HOTEL
Little Hemingfold Farmhouse Hotel
TN33 0TT. Tel: (042 46) 4338
17th century farmhouse set in 40 acres of fields and woods overlooking a two acre trout lake.
BEDROOMS: 1 Single, (1 TV, 1 phone, 1 tea/coffee) B&B £ 25.00 - £ 30.00. 7 Double, (6 en suite, 7 TV, 7 phone, 7 tea/

LITTLE HEMINGFOLD FARMHOUSE HOTEL

coffee) B&B £ 22.50 - £ 30.00. 4 Twin, (4 en suite, 4 TV, 4 phone, 4 tea/coffee) 1 Four Poster RESTAURANT: Traditional French Cuisine. Dinner: £ 15.00. House Wine: £ 6.00. HOTEL INFOR-MATION: CF. Sports Facilities: Golf nearby. Riding nearby. Trout fishing. Grass tennis. Swimming in lake. Croquet. Credit Cards: Ac. V.

Weekend Breaks: 2 nights: £ 68.00.

PUBLIC HOUSE
Black Horse
Hastings Road. Tel: (042 46) 3109

ᘛᘚ ᘛᘚ ᘛᘚ ᘛᘚ ᘛᘚ ᘛᘚ ᘛᘚ

TELSCOMBE
A small village set in a hollow of the downs. Telscombe was bequeathed to Brighton, and is held in trust so that it cannot be spoilt.
Population: 5,199 .

RESTAURANT
The Jewel in the Crown
379, South Coast Road. Tel: (0273) 582302

PUBLIC HOUSE
Telscombe Tavern
405, South Coast Road. Tel: (0273) 584674

ᘛᘚ ᘛᘚ ᘛᘚ ᘛᘚ ᘛᘚ ᘛᘚ ᘛᘚ

TICEHURST
Close to the county line, south of Bedgebury Forest, Ticehurst is a pleasant village with tile-hung houses. The inn is much older than it looks, and many of the houses are worth more than a cursory glance. In the 13th century church there is a 'doom window' showing devils carting souls off to hell.
Population: 2,899.

HOTEL
The Bell Hotel
High Street. Tel: (0580) 200234

RESTAURANT
Plantation Tea Co.
1 High Street. Tel: (0580) 200015

PUBLIC HOUSES
The Bull Inn
Three Leg Cross. Tel: (0580) 200586
The Chequers Inn
High Street. Tel: (0580) 200287
The Cherry Tree Inn
Dale Hill. Tel: (0580) 200337
Duke of York
The Square, High Street. Tel: (0580) 220229

OTHER AMENITIES
RIDING SCHOOL
Norwood Farm Cross Country Course
Norwood Farm. Tel: (0580) 200313

TAXI
Ticehurst Mini Cab Service
17 Springfields. Tel: (0580) 200180

ᘛᘚ ᘛᘚ ᘛᘚ ᘛᘚ ᘛᘚ ᘛᘚ ᘛᘚ

UCKFIELD
Though it is difficult to detect where Maresfield ends and Uckfield begins, it has recently been rescued from the modern plague by a good by-pass. A mixed High Street of some Georgian, but mostly unremarkable 20th century buildings. A commuter town.
Population: 9,064.

PLACES OF INTEREST
Beeches Farm
16th century tile-hung farmhouse. Sunken gardens, fine views, yew trees, lawns and roses.
Months Open: All year. Days Open: Every day. Hours Open: 10am - 5pm. Admission: 75p. House visits are by appointment only.

HOTELS
Hooke Hall
250 High Street. Tel: (0825) 761578
BEDROOMS: 1 Single, (1 en suite, 1 TV, 1 phone, 1 tea/coffee) 2 Double, (2 en suite, 2 TV, 2 phone, 2 tea/coffee) 3 Twin, (3 en suite, 3 TV, 3 phone, 3 tea/coffee) RESTAURANT: English/ Continental Cuisine. Dinner: £ 18.75. House Wine: £ 7.50. Specialities: Home made pasta. Credit Cards: Ac.

Ye Maidens Head Hotel
High Street. Tel: (0825) 762019

RESTAURANTS
Cains Restaurant
228 High Street. Tel: (0825) 761279
The Charcoal Grill
158 High Street. Tel: (0825) 767633
Chengs House
39 Framfield Road. Tel: (0825) 762514
Curry Centre, Tandoori Restaurant
55 High Street. Tel: (0825) 762878
The Highlands Inn & Restaurant
Ridgewood. Tel: (0825) 762989
Lucky House
226 High Street. Tel: (0825) 764156
Manor Park Fish & Chips
34 Browns Lane. Tel: (0825) 762014
The Oven Door
204 High Street. Tel: (0825) 763029
Sheffield Coach House
Sheffield Green. Tel: (0825) 790245
Weald Fish Bars
42 Framfield Road. Tel: (0825) 764489

PUBLIC HOUSES
Chalk & Cheese
119 High Street. Tel: (0825) 761366
The Peacock Inn
Shortbridge. Tel: (0825) 762463
The Prince Regent
High Street. Tel: (0825) 762009

CAFÉ/TEA ROOMS
The Geranium
16 Church Street. Tel: (0825) 764405

OTHER AMENITIES
ART GALLERIES
The Ashdown Gallery
70 Newtown High Street. Tel: (0825) 767180
Barnes Gallery
8 Church Street. Tel: (0825) 762066

CAR HIRE/CHAUFFEUR DRIVEN
Hedleys
32 Browns Lane, Manor Park. Tel: (0825) 767881

CINEMA
Picture House
High Street. Tel: (0825) 763822

GARDEN CENTRE

Cornwells
109 High Street. Tel: (0825) 762970

HEALTH CLUB
Gardens Dance and Beauty Centre
Kings Court, rear 164 High Street. Tel: (0825) 767310

HOSPITAL
Uckfield Hospital
High Street. Tel: (0825) 762175

HOSTEL
Youth Hostels Association (England & Wales)
Blackboys. Tel: (082 582) 607

LEISURE CENTRE
Utopia Leisure Centre
Downsview Crescent. Tel: (0825) 761722

STORE
Woolworths plc
High Street. Tel: (0825) 762545

TAXIS
G. Martin
12 Mill Drive. Tel: (0825) 762445
Minicabs
The Taxi Office, Link House, Bus Dept., Bell Lane. Tel: (0825) 765322
P.J. Private Hire
10 Mount Pleasant, Framfield Road. Tel: (0825) 762253
R & J Motors
122 The Drive, Church Coombe. Tel: (0825) 768000
Rimons Private Hire Car Service
6 Lime Close. Tel: (0825) 76287
Station Cars
Uckfield Railway Station. Tel: (0825) 765885

☙ ☙ ☙ ☙ ☙ ☙ ☙

UDIMORE
Due west of Rye just above the flood plain of two rivers, the Brede and the Tillingham. St Mary's church has Norman origins.
Population: 324.

HOTEL
The Hammonds Country Hotel
Tel: (0797) 223167/225070/225020

GUEST HOUSE
Vine Farm
The Vines. Tel: (0424) 882182

PUBLIC HOUSES

The Kings Head
Tel: (0424) 882349
*Free House. Opening Hours: 11.00-3.00/6.00-11.00. OPEN
ALL DAY SAT. Beer available: Real Ales, Lagers, Kegs. Food
Available: During opening hours. Garden. Children's area.Car
Park.Traditional games: Pool.*
The Plough Inn
Tel: (0797) 223381

❧ ❧ ❧ ❧ ❧ ❧ ❧

UPPER DICKER

Two and a half miles west of Hailsham. Holy
Trinity church is made of flint, in the Norman style,
although it is much more modern, having been
restored in 1843.

PLACES OF INTEREST

Michelham Priory
Tel: (0323) 844224
Founded in 1229, this Augustinian Priory is surrounded
by one of the largest moats in England. Musical instru-
ments, local history, glass, tapestry embroidery collection.
Working watermill, grinding wholemeal flour. Elizabe-
than wing and 14th century gatehouse.
*Months Open: March - October. Days Open: Everyday. Hours
Open: 11am - 5pm. Admission: £2.00. Children half price.
Licensed restaurants in grounds. Special exhibitions and events.*

RESTAURANT

Michelham Priory Restaurant
Tel: (0323) 844513

PUBLIC HOUSE

The Plough Inn
Tel: (0323) 844859

❧ ❧ ❧ ❧ ❧ ❧ ❧

VINES CROSS

A tiny Wealden village south-east of Heathfield,
grouped around a minor crossroads.

PUBLIC HOUSE

Brewers Arms
Tel: (043 53) 2288

OTHER AMENITY

GARDEN CENTRE
Rivermead Nursery
Tel: (043 53) 3353

WADHURST

This town has some fine buildings on its main
street, and in the surrounding countryside. A centre
of the ironworks industry, the church has iron
grave 'stones', and iron features throughout.
Wadhurst hosted the last important prize fight in
England in 1863.
Population: 4,390.

HOTELS

The Four Keys
Station Hill. Tel: (089 288) 2252
Williams Hotel & Residential
Buckhurst Place, Buckhurst Lane. Tel: (089 288) 3181

RESTAURANTS

Old Vine Restaurant
Cousley Wood. Tel: (089 288) 2271
Sonar Gaon Tandoori Restaurant
The Posthorne, High Street. Tel: (089 288) 3180

PUBLIC HOUSES

Best Beech Hotel
Best Beech Hill. Tel: (089 288) 2046
The Greyhound Hotel
St. James Square. Tel: (089 288) 3224
Rock Robin Hotel
Station Hill. Tel: (089 288) 2312
The White Hart
High Street. Tel: (089 288) 2878

OTHER AMENITIES

CAR HIRE/SELF DRIVE
Goldcrest Car Hire (Kent) Ltd.
Station Hill. Tel: (089 288) 3210

TAXIS
D.E. Brown
93 Queens Cottage. Tel: (089 288) 3121
Rainbow Taxis
Central Garage, Cousley Wood. Tel: (089 288) 3079

❧ ❧ ❧ ❧ ❧ ❧ ❧

WALDRON

An isolated village in the Weald south-west of
Heathfield. Possingworth Park to the north was
the estate of a 19th century art collector, built in
1866 for the then colossal sum of £60,000.
Population: 3,168.

PUBLIC HOUSE

The Star Inn
Tel: (043 53) 2495

WALLCROUCH

OTHER AMENITIES

GARDEN CENTRE
Inside Out
Tel: (0580) 200399

TAXI
Wadhurst Taxis
High Street. Tel: (0580) 200575

🐝 🐝 🐝 🐝 🐝 🐝 🐝

WARBLETON

East of Horam, this is little more than a magnificent church. It has now been joined by Rushlake Green to form a more substantial habitation.
Population: 1,078.

HOTEL

The Priory Country House Hotel
Stone House. Tel: (0435) 830553

PUBLIC HOUSE

Warbill in Tun Inn
Tel: (0435) 830636

🐝 🐝 🐝 🐝 🐝 🐝 🐝

WARTLING

The church contains some interesting examples of box pews.
Population: 495.

PUBLIC HOUSE

The Lamb Inn
Tel: (0323) 832116

🐝 🐝 🐝 🐝 🐝 🐝 🐝

WESTDEAN

The flint rectory is probably Norman, and as such, one of the oldest inhabited houses in the county.
Population: 75.

PLACES OF INTEREST

Charleston Manor
A beautiful manor house in a near-perfect setting. Its foundations are Norman. Open to the public during the summer.

🐝 🐝 🐝 🐝 🐝 🐝 🐝

WESTFIELD

Sitting in a high position north-east of Hastings and no doubt soon to be swallowed up. It will be no great loss, having suffered badly at the hands of the Victorians.
Population: 2,298.

RESTAURANT

Casual Cuisine Bistrobar
Woodgate House, Church Lane. Tel: (0424) 751137

PUBLIC HOUSES

The New Inn
Main Road. Tel: (0424) 751603
The Plough Inn
The Moor. Tel: (0424) 751066

OTHER AMENITY

TAXI
Westfield Mini-Cab Service
1 Robertson House, Main Road. Tel: (0424) 753229

🐝 🐝 🐝 🐝 🐝 🐝 🐝

WESTHAM

No more than a mile from the suburbs of Eastbourne, near Pevensey, it will be a shame when this lovely village church is subsumed into the town.
Population: 2,533.

PUBLIC HOUSE

Pevensey Castle Hotel
High Street. Tel: (0323) 761041

CAFÉ/TEA ROOMS

Swan Lake Cafe
6, High Street. Tel: (0323) 766971

🐝 🐝 🐝 🐝 🐝 🐝 🐝

WHATLINGTON

Quite secluded, just north of Battle, on the banks of the River Brede, with a small Early English church with a Victorian steeple.
Population: 286.

GUEST HOUSE

Leeford Place Guest House
Mill Lane. Tel: (042 46) 2863

PUBLIC HOUSE

Royal Oak
Tel: (042 487) 492

THE LONG MAN AT WILMINGTON

WILLINGDON

A suburb to the north of Eastbourne. Opposite St Mary's church is a group of buildings known as the Hooe designed by Lutyens in 1902. Willingdon was the birth place of Edward Clarke, traveller and collector.
Population: 5,896.

PLACES OF INTEREST

Hooe
A group of houses opposite the church built by Lutyens in 1902.

PUBLIC HOUSES

The Seven Sisters
Seven Sisters Road. Tel: (0323) 502165

The Wheatsheaf Inn
Church Street. Tel: (0323) 502069

CAFÉ/TEA ROOMS

Willingdon Bakery & Coffee Shop
5, Freshwater Square. Tel: (0323) 508786

WILMINGTON

Most famous for its 'long man' carved into the chalk of the downs, Wilmington also boasts one of the finest village streets in the county. Outside the Norman church is an ancient yew tree, buttressed and chained, possibly older than the building itself, near the site of a medieval Priory.
Population: 213.

PLACES OF INTEREST

Wilmington Priory
Tel: (0323) 870537
Remains of a 13th century Priory built on land given by Robert de Mortain, half brother of William the Conqueror, to the Abbot of Grestein. A collection of agricultural implements and farmhouse utensils.
Months Open: March - October. Days Open: Monday - Sunday (except Tuesday). Hours Open: Mon- Sat 11am-5.30pm; Sundays 2 - 5.30pm. Admission: 80p. Children half price.

HOTEL

Crossways Restaurant and Hotel
Crossways , Lewes Road. Tel: (032 12) 2455

114

THE STRAND GATE, WINCHELSEA

PUBLIC HOUSES

Sussex Ox
Milton Street. Tel: (0323) 870840

The Wilmington Arms
The Street. Tel: (0323) 870207

OTHER AMENITY

GARDEN CENTRE

Long Man Gardens
Tel: (0323) 870816

🐄 🐄 🐄 🐄 🐄 🐄

WINCHELSEA

Although badly battered by the French and the sea, this historic town is extremely pretty, especially in summer when the roses in the gardens are in full bloom. Another hill town (see Lewes and Rye), and also another of the Cinque Ports, Winchelsea differs from its near neighbour Rye in the peace that it manages to exude. It is largely pedestrianised, giving visitors time to appreciate its weatherboarded and tile-hung houses, and laid out on a well-defined grid system. Once much larger than it is now, and much more important to the nation's defences, with a huge fleet, Winchelsea seems glad of the respite.

PLACES OF INTEREST

Winchelsea Museum
Court Hall.
Collections illustrating the history of Winchelsea and the Cinque Ports. Archaeological specimens, models, maps, documents and handicraft.
Months Open: May - September.

HOTELS

The New Inn
German Street. Tel: (0797) 226252

Winchelsea Lodge Motel
Hastings Road. Tel: (0797) 226211

GUEST HOUSE

The Strand House
Tel: (0797) 226276

RESTAURANT

Finches
12 High Street. Tel: (0797) 226234

115

PUBLIC HOUSES

The Bridge Inn
The Strand. Tel: (0797) 224302
Ship Inn
Winchelsea Beach. Tel: (0797) 226686

OTHER AMENITY

CARAVAN PARK
Ferryfields
Station Road. Tel: (0797) 226344
Caravan Holiday Home Park (Private and Hire)
Months Open: Occupation March to October inclusive. Beautiful private holiday park with fishing river, close to BR station and lying alongside ancient Winchelsea town. Proprietors: Mrs M P Giddings.

WINCHELSEA BEACH

Close to the original site of the town, which used to stand on a spit of land, and was washed away in a great storm of 1287, becoming 'Old Winchelsey Drowned'. It was then that the new town was built on the hill one mile inland.

PUBLIC HOUSE

Club 31
Broadwater Dogs Hill Road. Tel: (0797) 225965

CAFÉ/TEA ROOMS

White Lodge Cafe
Pett Level Road. Tel: (0797) 226519

OTHER AMENITIES

CARAVAN PARKS
Haven Holidays Ltd
Winchelsea Sands Caravan Park, Pett Level Road.
Tel: (0797) 226442
Rye Bay Caravan Park Ltd.
Pett Level Road. Tel: (0797) 226340
Stanhope Caravan Park
Sunset View. Tel: (0797) 226526

WITHYHAM

The church contains a memorial to Vita Sackville-West, and although some miles distant, this rural village is almost an appendage of Knole, the Sackville seat in Kent. Even the pub, the Dorset Arms, is named after the Earl of Dorset, Lord Sackville. *Population: 4,120.*

PUBLIC HOUSE

Dorset Arms Hotel
Tel: (089 277) 770278

WIVELSFIELD

A small village two miles outside Burgess Hill, paired with Wivelsfield Green.
Population: 1,440.

PLACES OF INTEREST

Great Ote Hall
Built at the end of the 16th century, an unusually small country house with an impressive set of tall chimneys.

PUBLIC HOUSE

The Cock Inn
North Common Road. Tel: (044 484) 668

OTHER AMENITY

CAR HIRE
Inter Primos Chauffeur Service
Wivelsfield Hall. Tel: (0444) 84223

WOODSIDE

Situated in the flat fen-land north of Rye, very close to the Kent border.

OTHER AMENITY

GARDEN CENTRE
A.C. Harman
Woodside Nurseries, Quickbourne Lane.
Tel: (079 74) 2520

WYCH CROSS

In the middle of the Ashdown Forest, at the intersection of five roads. To the south is a clump of trees and a stone slab commemorating a visit by President Kennedy to the home of Harold Macmillan, later the Earl of Stockton, at Chelwood Gate.

HOTEL

Roebuck Hotel
Tel: (034 282) 3811

OTHER AMENITY

GARDEN CENTRE
Wych Cross Nurseries & Garden Centre
Tel: (034 282) 2705

THE SACKVILLE MONUMENT, WITHYAM CHURCH

PEVENSEY CASTLE

AFK: A.F. Kirsting. EH: English Heritage. NT: National Trust.

THE BARBICAN, LEWES CASTLE

Place of Interest	Town	Page No
Clergy House	Alfriston	7
Saxon Cemetery	Alfriston	7
Shelley's Folly	Barcombe	9
Battle Abbey	Battle	10
Battle Museum	Battle	10

Place of Interest	Town	Page No
Museum of Shops and Social History		
	Battle	10
Bexhill Museum	Bexhill-on-Sea	12
Bexhill Museum of Costume & Social History		
	Bexhill-on-Sea	12

HERSTMONCEUX CASTLE

INDEX OF AMENITIES/OPEN ALL DAY

THEATRES & CONCERT HALLS

TOURIST OFFICES

ZOOS

PUBS OPEN ALL DAY

QUESTIONNAIRE

In the compilation of this guide, it is inevitable that there will be errors, omissions, duplications, and wrong dialling codes, although we have made every effort to eliminate them. In the most part this due to the march of time, restaurants close, or change their names, and although we did send every establishment listed a form that they could check and if necessary amend the data, not everyone returned the form. The information in italics listed below certain establishments has been supplied by themselves, and should be accurate.

It is our stated intention to create as accurate a database, and therefore guide book, as possible, and in this pursuit we would invite readers and contributors to send in details of omissions or incorrect listings on the form below (please photocopy it and return it to us). We would also be most interested in any editorial corrections or additions, any fact or legend associated with anywhere listed.

Please Photocopy the form, complete and return it to:
Gaymer's Guides, 24 Notting Hill Gate, London W11 3BR.

TOWN _____

EDITORIAL DETAILS _____

_____

_____

_____

_____

ESTABLISHMENT NAME _____

ADDRESS _____

TELEPHONE _____

OTHER DETAILS _____

DID YOU FIND THE GUIDE USEFUL? _____

DO YOU HAVE ANY SUGGESTIONS ON HOW IT COULD BE
IMPROVED? _____

_____

COMMENTS _____

_____

NAME _____

ADDRESS _____

TELEPHONE _____

DATE _____

SIGNED _____

INDEX OF TOWNS